Manufacturing Technology for Higher Technicians

W. Bolton

Heinemann Newnes

Heinemann Newnes
An imprint of Heinemann Professional Publishing Ltd
Halley Court, Jordan Hill, Oxford OX2 8EJ

OXFORD   LONDON   MELBOURNE   AUCKLAND   SINGAPORE
IBADAN   NAIROBI   GABORONE   KINGSTON

First published as *Manufacturing Technology* 4 by Butterworths 1985
First published by Heinemann Professional Publishing Ltd 1989

British Library Cataloguing in Publication Data
Bolton, W. (William)
    Manufacturing technology for higher technicians
    1. Production engineering
    I. Title
    670.42   TS176

ISBN 0 434 90227 6

Printed and bound by Hartnolls Limited
Bodmin, Cornwall

Preface

This book has been written with the following aims:

1. To present an overview of the manufacturing processes commonly used.
2. To enable an informed choice of manufacturing process to be made, taking into account the various alternatives possible.
3. To enable the cost factor to be taken into account in determining which manufacturing method to use for a product.

The text covers the BTEC Manufacturing Technology unit at HNC/HND level. If this unit were to have a subtitle it would be 'an introduction to the selection of manufacturing processes'. The book can also be used as a general reference text for other courses involving manufacturing processes.

W. Bolton

Contents

1 Costing

After working through this chapter you should be able to:

Identify the cost elements in the price of a component.
Explain the difference between standard and historical costing.
Calculate direct labour costs, direct material costs and overhead costs to arrive at a production cost.
Explain how production overheads can be allocated and recovered.
Explain the term 'variance'.
Calculate cutting speeds, machine operation times and tool life.
Calculate tooling costs.
Calculate the most economical cutting speed.

1.1 COST ACCOUNTING

There is a demand for product X, what price should we charge? How much does it cost to manufacture X?

How profitable is it for the company to manufacture and sell product Y? Would it be more profitable to make X instead of Y?

What financial resources will the company need to support its production during the next year? How can the company tell if it is overshooting the budget and what aspects of the production are responsible for the overshoot?

The above are some of the types of questions that could be posed in a company and which cost accounting is designed to answer. *Cost accounting* can be defined, according to the Institute of Cost and Management Accountants, as

'The application of accounting and costing principles, methods and techniques in the ascertainment of costs and the analysis of savings and/or excesses as compared with previous experience or with standards.'

In this chapter the aim is to introduce the reader to the basic elements involved in arriving at manufacturing costs so that the importance of costing in any manufacturing organisation can be appreciated. For more detailed information readers should refer to the many books on cost accounting; for example, *Principles of Cost Accounting* by C.J. Walker (MacDonald and Evans, 1982).

1.2 THE PRICE OF A PRODUCT

The selling price of a product can be considered to be made up of the following elements:

1 Prime costs These are the costs of the material and labour directly involved in the manufacture of the product. Costs are said to be *direct costs* when they can be separately identified as relating to the product concerned. Thus the direct material cost is the cost of the materials consumed or incorporated in the production of the product. The direct labour cost is the cost of the labour directly involved in the production process.

2 Production overheads In addition to the prime production costs there are production overheads. For instance, in the prime costs no allowance has been made for the cost of the machinery involved in the production process, only the material and labour costs having been taken into account. In addition there are such cost items as electrical power, lighting, factory maintenance, storekeeping, management, etc. This type of cost is called an *indirect cost*, such costs being difficult to charge to particular products.

Elements 1 and 2 can be considered to represent the total production costs for a product.

3 General administration and selling overheads These overheads include the costs of distribution and marketing of the product and general administration costs incurred in the company.

Elements 1, 2 and 3 constitute the total cost to the company of the product.

4 Profit This is the amount the company decide to add to the produce cost in order to give the selling price.

Figure 1.1 illustrates how the above elements are combined to give the selling price. In this book we are concerned with those elements—i.e. the prime costs and the production overheads— that are responsible for the production, or manufacturing, costs.

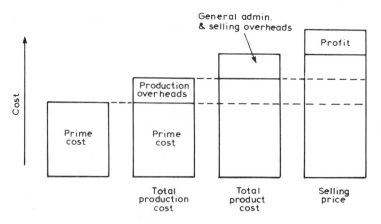

Figure 1.1 The cost elements in the selling price of a product

Standard and historical costing   With *standard costing* the costs are estimated before the production occurs and are prepared on the basis of standards that have been predetermined for materials and labour. For *historical costing* the costs are determined after the production has occurred. These costs are obtained from records taken during the processing of the materials and labour used.

Standard costing enables the management to exercise cost control in that the actual costs, and the factors determining those costs, can be compared with the standards set. This type of costing is widely used where there is repetitive manufacture, e.g. where the production department have frequently to make the same or similar products. In such situations the standards are obtained from past experience of manufacturing the same or similar work and thus the cost of production can be established.

Where a one-off product is involved or where few processes that have previously been used will be adopted for a new product, the use of standard costing may possibly be too expensive. The reasons for this could be that before it can be used measurements would have to be made of the times taken for workers to complete the various aspects of the production, the materials used, etc.

Direct labour costs   With historical costing the direct labour costs can be obtained from time records kept by each person involved in a particular job and the labour rates. Thus on some jobs there might be 10 hours of capstan lathe work, 5 hours drilling, 10 hours grinding, etc. The cost is then found by multiplying each of the times by the labour rate for each machine operator. For example, if the labour rate for the capstan lathe work was £5 per hour then the cost of 10 hours work would be £50. If the labour rate for the drilling was £4 per hour then the cost for the drilling would have been £20. By taking account of the times spent by each person in the production process then the total direct labour cost can be determined.

With standard costing the direct labour cost is found from the standard times, adjusted for the target level of operator performance, and the labour rates. The *standard time* for a job can be defined as the time needed for a qualified worker to carry out the job at a defined level of performance. Such times are determined by *work measurement*. This may involve an investigator in directly observing a worker carrying out the job and timing the various segments of the job in addition to estimating the general tempo of the work, and hence the time possible with the 'standard' worker.

Another method that is often used is to make use of the fact that many jobs are made up of elements that are common to other jobs—elements for which standard times already exist. By breaking up the new job into its constituent elements the standard time can be determined by adding together the standard times for each of the elements.

Operator performance is a measure of how a worker compares with the performance expected of the 'standard' worker. An operator rated as being 100 is equivalent to the standard worker. An operator rated at less than 100 is expected to perform at a higher rate than the standard worker while an operator rated at greater than 100 works slower than the standard worker. A 100 rated worker thus needs 100% of the standard time for the job; a 90 rated worker requires 90% of the standard time, and a 110 rated worker requires 110% of the standard time. If the standard time for a job is 50 minutes then a worker rated at 110 would be expected to take $50 \times 110/100 = 55$ minutes for the job.

The standard costing for a job that, say, involves 4 hours standard time with an operator rated at 110 when the labour rate is £5 per hour is thus:

standard cost = standard time × operator rating × labour rate

$$= 4 \times \frac{110}{100} \times 5 = £22$$

Direct material cost   Where materials are bought specifically for a particular job then the actual price of the materials can be charged to that job and so the direct material cost obtained. However, materials are often bought for a store and then issued from the store as required by the production, the storekeeper re-ordering materials as and when required to maintain the appropriate stock levels.

Because the material in store may have resulted from a number of different purchases, at different prices, then it may not be possible to state what the actual cost of the material is that is used in a particular job. In such circumstances a number of different methods are used for costing. These are:

1   First in, first out (FIFO)
It is assumed that the first material to enter the store is the first material that will be used and so the cost of the oldest material, in the appropriate type, is used. Thus suppose the following were the purchases made for a particular material:

Date	Units purchased	Price per unit
June 1	100	£1.00
June 18	100	£1.20
July 1	200	£1.40

If the production department on June 6 required 60 units of the material, then the cost would be at £1.00 per unit, giving a total cost of £60. If now, on June 20, the production department required 100 units of the material, then the cost would be reckoned on the basis of 40 units at £1.00 per unit and the remaining 60 at £1.20 per unit. This would give a total cost of £112.

2   Last in, first out (LIFO)
With this method the cost is taken as being that of the most recent purchase, it being assumed that it is the most recently purchased material which is being used. Thus, from the data given above, the material drawn from the store on June 20 would all have been charged at £1.20 per unit—a total cost of £120 for 100 units.

3   Highest in, first out
With this method the cost is taken as being that of the most highly priced purchase, regardless of the date the material was purchased. For example, suppose the following were the purchases made for a particular material:

Date	Units purchased	Price per unit
June 1	100	£1.00
June 18	100	£1.20
July 1	100	£1.10

Then, if on July 2, the production department wanted 150 units of the material, the cost would be given as £1.20 per unit despite the fact that not all the material was purchased at that rate.

4   Average cost
With this method an average price is used for all the stock of a

particular material. Thus for the data previously given, the average price is £1.10 per unit. If, on July 2, the production department wanted 150 units then the cost would be £1.10 per unit.

5 Market price

With this method the cost is given as the market price of the material on the date the material is taken from the store, irrespective of the material not having been purchased for the store on that day and at that price.

6 Standard cost

With this system the material issued by the store is at a standard cost. This is a cost that has been assumed for the material and is not necessarily the real price paid for the material. Until the standard is revised, all the material is issued at the standard cost, regardless of the price paid.

7 Replacement pricing

Here the cost is the price that it is anticipated will have to be paid to replace the material when it is reordered.

Where standard costing is used for the entire product, both materials and labour, then the standard material cost is used. In other situations, however, the average cost is most used for materials costs.

The following example illustrates how the standard material cost could be worked out for a product.

Material weight used in product	0.40 kg
Standard cost of material	£1.10 per kg
Standard material cost	1.10 × 0.40 = £0.44

Overheads   Overheads are costs which cannot be specifically allocated to any particular job. These could include: costs of tools; indirect labour, such as supervision; quality control; transport and technical services; general costs such as management, maintenance, power and welfare; and standing costs such as rent, rates, depreciation and insurance.

In order that these charges can be recovered, a method has to be adopted of sharing the overhead costs between the products. There are essentially four methods by which the overheads costs can be apportioned:

1. According to the direct labour cost;
2. According to the direct labour hours;
3. According to the machine hours involved;
4. According to the number of units of product produced.

Where overheads are apportioned according to the *direct labour cost*, this is estimated for the production department over, say, one year and all the overhead cost put against it. For example, if the total direct labour cost for one year is £100 000 and the total overheads is £60 000, then for every £1.00 of direct labour an overhead of £0.60 is charged. This amount is known as the *direct labour cost rate*. If a product has a direct labour cost of £100 then the overheads to be charged to that product are £60. This method is often used where the production process is labour intensive.

Where the overheads are apportioned according to the *direct labour hours*, these are estimated for the production department over, say, one year and all the overhead cost put against it. For example, if the total direct labour hours for one year are 20 000 hours and the total overheads is £60 000, then for every 1 hour direct labour an overhead of £3 is charged. This amount is known as the *direct labour hour rate*. If a product has a direct labour time of 4 hours then the indirect cost is £12.

Where the overheads are apportioned according to the *machine hours*, the total number of machine hours is estimated over a period for a particular machine or a group of similar machines. This number of hours could be either the number of hours for which the machine or group is expected to be operated or the number of hours which would be operated when they are used at normal capacity. Thus if, say, the total machine hours for one year for a particular group of machines is 80 000 hours and the overhead cost estimated for that group of machines is £40 000, then for 1 hour of machine time an overhead of £2 is charged. Hence if a product requires a time of 3 hours on those machines then the indirect cost is £6. The rate at which the overheads are charged against the machine hours is known as the *machine hour rate*.

$$\text{Machine hour rate} = \frac{\text{overheads}}{\text{machine hours}}$$

The following example illustrates the use of the machine hour rate to a costing for a product.

Process	Cost centre	Hours	Labour cost	Machine hour rate	Overhead cost
Machining	R	2.0	£4.00	£4.60	£ 9.20
Drilling	R	1.0	£2.00	£4.60	£ 4.60
Finishing	S	0.5	£1.00	£3.00	£ 1.50
Final assembly	T	1.5	£1.00	£2.50	£ 3.75
		Totals	£8.00		£19.05

Production cost:		
	Direct material cost	£12.00
	Direct labour cost	£ 8.00
	Overheads	£19.05
	Total	£39.05

In the above example note that both different labour rates and machine hour rates may be used for different types of process, the cost centre coding indicating the cost rates that are to be used.

In working out the overheads that are to be charged against a particular machine or group of machines in order to obtain the machine hour rate, each type of overhead is taken and apportioned to the machine or group according to some appropriate measure. Thus rents, rates and general depreciation of the buildings may be charged on the basis of the floor space occupied by the machine, due allowances being made for gangways. Supervisor costs may be spread over the range of machines that are supervised. General costs such as heating and lighting may be charged according to the floor space occupied by the machine. Machine depreciation, maintenance, repair, tooling costs, etc. can be allocated as an overhead charge to the machine concerned.

The machine hour rate is often used where the production processes are highly mechanised and a high percentage of the overheads is due to depreciation of the machinery and tooling costs in general. As indicated earlier, if the production process had been labour intensive rather than machine intensive the direct labour cost would have been more appropriate rather than machine hours as the basis for charging overheads.

Another method that can be used for charging overheads is by the *number of units of product*. The total number of units of product is estimated for, say, one year and all the overhead cost put against it. For example, if the total number of units of product in a year is estimated at 20 000 and the total overheads is £40 000, then for each unit of product there is an overhead cost of £2.

Direct labour cost and machine hours are probably the most common methods of charging overheads in production situations and, in general, it is the most dominant element in the overheads which determines the method used. A highly mechanised production process will probably incur most of its overheads as a result of machine depreciation and tooling costs. In such a situation the best basis for charging the overheads is machine hours as it is likely that the greater the length of machine time the greater the overheads.

Standard overhead cost rate

When standard costing is used a standard cost rate is generally employed for the overheads. The basis used for calculating the overheads can be any of the methods referred to earlier, i.e. direct labour cost, direct labour hours, machine hours, units of product.

The *standard overhead cost rate* is the rate determined by dividing the expected overhead cost attributable to a particular cost centre by the predetermined quantity of the base, e.g. machine hours, to which the rate is applied. The difference between the standard and the historical overhead cost rate is that the standard rate is determined by the expected overhead cost rather than the overhead cost that has occurred.

Thus, for example, a company may estimate that overheads of £20 000 are to be expected for a particular cost centre, with 4000 machine hours taking place. The standard overhead cost rate is thus £5 per machine hour. If now a standard costing is required for a product involving an expectation of 4 hours of machine work then the overhead cost will be £20.

In order to show, as a comparison, the two most popular methods, the following example illustrates the application of direct labour cost and machine hours as the basis for determining overheads and hence the standard cost of a product.

A company has estimated that over one year the production department will have:

Direct labour cost of	£100 000
Machine hours of	40 000
Overhead costs of	£ 60 000

A batch of products is estimated to have:

Direct labour costs of   £2000
Direct material costs of   £4000
Machine hours of   100

Estimate the standard production cost of the batch if the over-heads are to be charged on the basis of (a) direct labour cost and (b) machine hours.

(a) The overhead cost per pound of direct labour cost is

$$\frac{60\,000}{100\,000} = \text{£0.60 per £1 of direct labour}$$

Hence the overhead cost for the production batch is

$$2000 \times 0.60 = \text{£1200}$$

The total cost of the batch is therefore

Direct labour cost   £2000
Direct material cost   £4000
Overheads   £1200
Total cost   £7200

(b) The overhead cost per machine hour is

$$\frac{60\,000}{4000} = \text{£15 per machine hour}$$

Hence the overhead cost for the production batch is

$$100 \times 15 = \text{£1500}$$

The total cost of the batch is therefore

Direct labour cost   £2000
Direct material cost   £4000
Overheads   £1500

Total cost   £7500

Variance With standard costing, the costs are estimated before they are incurred and thus there may be differences between the estimated and the incurred costs. The difference between the actual and the estimated performance, whether it be sales, labour costs, materials costs, etc is known as the *variance*. A negative variance means that the actual performance is under the estimated amount, a positive variance means the actual performance is greater than that estimated. The two examples below illustrate this.

A cost centre in the production department estimated that for a particular batch of products their direct labour costs would be £6000. The actual direct labour costs were later found to be £6450. There is thus a direct labour cost variance of +£450.

A cost centre estimated that the direct materials costs for a batch of products would be £4200. The actual direct materials costs were later found to be £4120. There is thus a direct materials cost variance of −£80.

1.3 CUTTING SPEED

Cutting speed is defined as the rate at which the cutting edge of a tool passes over the work and is generally expressed in metres per minute. Thus in the case of a drilling operation, one rotation of the drill moves the cutting edge over the workpiece a distance equal to the circumference of the drill, i.e. πD, where D is the drill diameter. Hence in one minute, if the drill is rotating at N rev/min, then the distance covered is $N\pi D$. The cutting speed is therefore $N\pi D$. The following example illustrates the use of this relationship.

How many revolutions per minute should a 12 mm diameter drill rotate at if a cutting speed of 25 m/min is to be obtained?

In order to be consistent on units distances are put in metres and time in minutes. Hence

$$\text{Cutting speed} = 25 = N \times \pi \times 12 \times 10^{-3}$$

Hence $\qquad N = 663 \text{ rev/min}$

Another continuous rotary machining process is milling. For such a process the same type of relationship holds as for drilling. Thus, if D is the diameter of the cutter and N the number of revolutions of that cutter per unit time, then the cutting speed is $N\pi D$. Thus the rate of revolution of the cutter necessary to give a cutting speed of 20 m/min when the cutter has a diameter of 100 mm is given by

$$\text{Cutting speed} = 20 = N \times \pi \times 100 \times 10^{-3}$$

$$N = 63.7 \text{ rev/min}$$

Machine operation times

With a continuous rotary cutting process,

$$\text{cutting speed } V = N\pi D$$

where N is the number of spindle revolutions per unit time and D is the diameter of the cutter. If V is in units of m/min, D in millimetres and N in rev/min, then

$$V = N\pi D \times 10^{-3}, \text{ i.e. } V = N\pi d/1000$$

This latter form is generally the form in which this equation is found in texts.

The movement given in machining per revolution of the spindle, or in non-rotary situations per reversal of the work, is known as the *feed rate*. Thus, in a drilling operation, the rate at which the drill travels through the workpiece is the feed rate. In milling, the feed rate is the rate at which the work advances past the cutter. If f is the feed rate, then for N revolutions per unit time of a spindle the distance moved by the drill through the workpiece, or the work past the cutter, in unit time is Nf. If N is in rev/min and f in mm/rev, then the distance moved in a minute is Nf mm. If L is the required length of cut then the time taken to achieve this cut is L/Nf.

$$\text{Time for 1 cut} = \frac{L}{Nf}$$

The following example illustrates the use of the above equation.

Calculate the time taken to drill a hole 12 mm diameter and 30 mm deep with a cutting speed of 20 m/min and a feed rate of 0.18 mm/rev.

$$V = N\pi D$$

$$\text{Hence, Time} = \frac{L\pi D}{Vf} = \frac{30 \times \pi \times 12}{20 \times 1000 \times 0.18}$$

Note that in this calculation all distances are in mm and all times in minutes.

$$\text{Hence,} \qquad \text{Time} = 0.31 \text{ min}$$

In milling the cutting speed is given by $V = N\pi D$, but an allowance called the approach distance A must be added to the length of the machined surface L_m to give the total length of cut L.

$$L = L_m + A$$

$$\text{Hence, Time for one cut} = \frac{L}{Nf} = \frac{L_m + A}{Nf}$$

For peripheral milling

$$A = \sqrt{[d(D - d)]}$$

where D is the diameter of the cutter and d the depth of cut.

For face milling

$$A = \tfrac{1}{2}D - \sqrt{(\tfrac{1}{4}D^2 - \tfrac{1}{4}b^2)}$$

where b is the width of cut and D the diameter of the cutter. Hence, using the above equations, the time taken for one cut by milling can be determined.

Similarly the times taken for other cutting operations can be determined. Thus it is possible, for the machining of some component involving perhaps a number of machining operations, to estimate the total machining time by working out the times for each part of the machining.

Cutting times are, however, only that time for which the tool is actually in contact with the workpiece during the metal removal process. No allowance is included for handling the workpiece, tool changing, relaxation time for the operator, etc. To find the standard time for the entire operation these other times must be taken into account. Only then does it become possible to work out how many components can be processed in any given time.

In general, the time for all the handling, machining and manipulating is made up of the following elements:

1 Initial setting up of the machine;
2 Loading and unloading the workpieces;
3 Manipulation of the machine during its operation, e.g. gear changing;
4 Machining time;
5 Measuring and gauging;
6 Changing and resetting tools;
7 Tool regrinding.
8 Contingency allowance for such factors as operator fatigue, etc.

For more information on the calculation of times taken, the reader is advised to consult the book *Principles of Engineering Production* by A.J. Lissaman and S.J. Martin (Hodder and Stoughton, 1982).

Tooling costs The greater the life of a tool the greater the period of time over which the tool cost can be spread and so the smaller the tooling cost overhead per job. If T is the *tool life* then the cost of tooling for a job is inversely proportional to T, i.e.

$$\text{tooling cost} \propto \frac{1}{T}$$

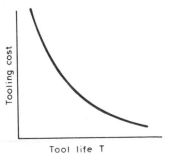

Figure 1.2 Tooling costs and tool life

Figure 1.2 shows the relationship graphically.

Tool life however depends on the cutting speed V. In cutting operations the relationship between cutting speed and the tool life is given by *Taylor's equastion*,

$$VT^n = C$$

where n is an index related to the type of material used for the cutting tool and C is a constant. Thus as $T = (C/V)^{1/n}$ the tooling cost is related to the cutting speed by

$$\text{tooling cost} \propto \frac{1}{T} \propto \frac{1}{(C/V)^{1/n}} \propto (C/V)^{1/n}$$

as C is a constant. *Figure 1.3* shows this relationship graphically.

The value of n depends on the cutting material used, typically it is about 0.1 to 0.15 for high speed steel tools, 0.2 to 0.4 for tungsten carbide tools and 0.4 to 0.6 for ceramic tools. To illustrate the effect on tooling cost of cutting speed, consider a tool for which n is 0.2 and the effect of changing the cutting speed from, say, 180 m/min to 90 m/min.

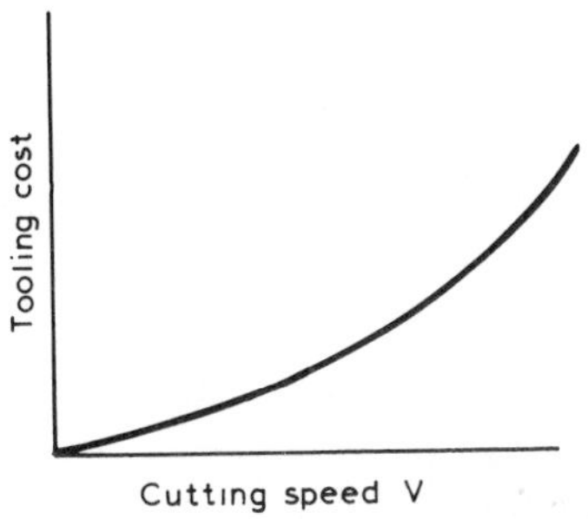

Tooling cost for 90 m/min $\propto 90^{1/0.2}$
Tooling cost for 180 m/min $\propto 180^{1/0.2}$

Hence, $\dfrac{\text{Tooling cost for 90 m/min}}{\text{Tooling cost for 180 m/min}} = \dfrac{90^{1/0.2}}{180^{1/0.2}}$

$$= \left(\frac{90}{180}\right)^{1/0.2} = 0.5^5 = 0.031$$

Figure 1.3 Tooling costs and cutting speed

The tooling cost at 90 m/min is thus considerably less than that at 180 m/min, being only 0.031 of the 180 m/min cost. Less it be thought that slower cutting speeds inevitably mean lower production cost, account has to be taken of the smaller number of components that can be machined per hour at the lower speed.

The higher the cutting speed the smaller the time required to remove the metal. As the cost of carrying out the cutting will be proportional to the time taken for the machining then so the higher the cutting speed the smaller the machining cost.

Cost of cutting $\propto$ time taken for the cutting

But, time taken for cutting $\propto 1/V$

where V is the cutting speed.

If the cutting speed is doubled then the time taken is halved.

Thus

Cost of cutting $\propto 1/V$

Figure 1.4 shows how the cost of cutting depends on the cutting speed. Also on the same graph the tooling cost as a function of cutting speed has been plotted (this is *Figure 1.3*). The total cost is the sum of the costs of cutting and the tooling cost and so can be obtained by adding the two graphs together. The composite graph shows a minimum at a particular cutting speed, this being the most economical cutting speed to use.

The following example illustrates the use of Taylor's equation in a costing. For a particular machining operation $n = 0.3$ and $C = 140$. The time taken to change the tool is 5 minutes and the time taken to regrind it, 4 minutes. The machine time per component is 8 minutes. The machine cost is £0.05 per minute. Ignoring workpiece handling times, setting times and tool depreciation, what is the cost of machining 100 components at a cutting speed of 60 m per minute?

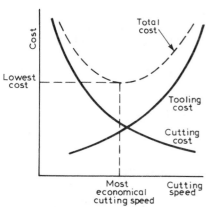

Figure 1.4 Total tooling cost

$$\text{Tool life } T = \left(\frac{C}{V}\right)^{1/n} = \left(\frac{140}{60}\right)^{1/0.3} = 16.4 \text{ min}$$

Therefore the number of components per regrind is

$$\frac{16.4}{8} = 2.05$$

The tool change cost $= 5 \times 0.05 = £0.25$

The tool change cost per component $= \dfrac{0.25}{2.05} = £0.12$

The tool regrind cost $= 4 \times 0.05 = £0.20$

The tool regrind cost per component $= \dfrac{0.20}{2.05} = £0.10$

The machining cost per component $= 8 \times 0.05 = £0.40$

Hence the total cost per component $= £0.12 + £0.10 + £0.40 = £0.62$

The cost therefore of a batch of 100 components $= £62$

Most economical cutting speed The following is a derivation of the relationship for the most economical cutting speed.

$$\text{Time to machine a unit volume of metal} \propto \frac{1}{V} = \frac{K}{V}$$

where V is the cutting speed and K a constant.

If H is the machining cost per minute (the time used is generally minutes rather than seconds), then

$$\text{Cost of machining a unit volume of metal} = \frac{HK}{V} \qquad (1)$$

with V being the speed in metres per minute.

In the time taken of (K/V) to machine unit volume of metal the number of tool changes will be

$$\text{Number of tool changes} = \frac{K}{TV}$$

where T is the tool life.

If J is the total cost per tool change then

$$\text{Tooling cost per unit volume of metal cut} = \frac{JK}{TV}$$

But, according to Taylor's equation, $VT^n = C$ or $T = (C/V)^{1/n}$.

Hence, Tooling cost per unit volume of metal cut =

$$\frac{JK}{V(C/V)^{1/n}} = \frac{JK(V)^{(1-n)/n}}{C^{1/n}} \qquad (2)$$

The total cost per unit volume of metal cut is the sum of the machining cost, equation (1), and the tooling cost, equation (2).

Hence, Total cost per unit volume of metal cut

$$\frac{HK}{V} + \frac{JK(V)^{(1-n)/n}}{C^{1/n}}$$

The minimum value of this cost P can be found by differentiating and equating to zero.

$$\frac{dP}{dV} = -\frac{HK}{V^2} + \left(\frac{1-n}{n}\right) \frac{JK}{C^{1/n}} (V)^{(1-2n)/n}$$

When this is equated to zero, as K is not zero, then:

$$\frac{H}{V^2} = \left(\frac{1-n}{n}\right) \frac{J}{C^{1/n}} (V)^{(1-2n)/n}$$

$$H = \left(\frac{1-n}{n}\right) \frac{J}{C^{1/n}} (V)^{1/n}$$

Hence

$$V = C \left(\frac{n}{(J/H)(1 - n)} \right)^{n}$$

The above is the condition for the most economical cutting speed.

The following example illustrates a use of the expression. The cost of operating a particular machine is £12 per hour and the cost of a tool change is £3. For the machining conditions concerned $C = 150$ and $n = 0.25$. What is the most economical cutting speed?

$$V = C \left(\frac{n}{(J/H)(1 - n)} \right)^{n}$$

$J = £3$ and $H = £12$ per hour $= £12/60$ per minute. Hence $J/H = 15$ min. Thus

$$V = 150 \left(\frac{0.25}{15 \times 0.75} \right)^{0.25}$$

$$= 57.9 \text{ m/min}$$

QUESTIONS

(1) Explain the differences between (a) direct and indirect costs; (b) prime and overhead costs.

(2) State the various cost elements that go to make up the selling price of a product.

(3) Explain the difference between historical and standard costing.

(4) Define the term standard time.

(5) Explain how the direct labour cost is obtained with standard costing.

(6) Calculate the standard direct labour cost for the product having the following standards:
Process A. Standard time 3 hours, operator rating 100, labour rate £4.00 per hour.
Process B. Standard time 1.2 hours, operator rating 90, labour rate £3.80 per hour.
Process C. Standard time 0.5 hours, operator rating 110, labour rate £3.00 per hour.

(7) Calculate the standard direct labour cost for the batch of products having the following standards:
Process A. Standard time 200 hours, operator rating 95, labour rate £4.50 per hour.
Process B. Standard time 320 hours, operator rating 110, labour rate £4.00 per hour.
Process C. Standard time 120 hours, operator rating 105, labour rate £3.50 per hour.

(8) Explain the various ways materials can be costed for a cost centre.

(9) Calculate the standard direct material cost for a product using the following materials:
Material A. Expected material required 2.5 kg, standard material cost £0.30 per kg.
Material B. Expected material required 1.2 kg, standard material cost £2.00 per kg.

(10) Calculate the standard direct material costs for a batch of products using the following materials:
Material A. Expected material required 200 kg, standard material cost £0.80 per kg.
Material B. Expected material required 800 kg, standard material cost £0.60 per kg.
Material C. Expected material required 200 kg, standard material cost £1.00 per kg.

(11) Explain how overheads costs can be recovered.

(12) Give examples of typical overheads that may occur for a production department cost centre.

(13) Explain how overhead costs are apportioned according to (a) direct labour cost, (b) machine hours.

(14) A production department is expected for a particular period of time to have direct labour hours of 1200 and overhead costs of £3600. What would be the estimated overhead cost for a product batch requiring 300 direct labour hours?

(15) A cost centre in a production department is expected for a particular period of time to have 1500 machine hours and overheads of £2500. What would be the expected overhead cost for a product requiring 40 machine hours at that cost centre?

(16) A cost centre in a production department is expected for a particular period of time to have direct labour costs of £20 000 and overhead costs of £40 000. What would be the estimated overhead cost for a product estimated as requiring direct labour costs of £400?

(17) Calculate the overhead cost and the total production cost for the following product, the overheads being costed on the basis of machine hours.

Process	Cost centre	Hours	Labour cost	Machine hour rate
Machining	A	2.5	£6.00	£5.00
Drilling	B	1.0	£2.60	£4.00
Finishing	C	1.5	£3.40	£4.50
Packing	D	0.5	£2.60	£3.00

Direct material cost £20.00

(18) Calculate the overhead cost and the total production cost for the following product, the overheads being costed on the basis of direct labour cost.

Process	Cost centre	Hours	Labour hour rate	Labour cost/hour
Assembly	A	2.5	£4.00	£5.00
Packing	B	0.5	£3.60	£4.00

Direct materials cost £12.00

(19) Under what circumstances would the allocation of overheads against machine hours be more appropriate than against direct labour hours?

(20) Explain the term standard overhead cost rate.

(21) A cost centre in the production department has been estimated as having the following costs over a quarter:

Direct labour cost	£20 000
Machine hours	5 000
Overhead costs	£ 4 000

A batch of products is estimated to require

Direct labour cost	£ 500
Direct material cost	£1400
Machine hours	800

Estimate the standard production cost of the batch if the overheads are to be charged on the basis of (a) direct labour cost and (b) machine hours.

(22) Explain the term variance.

(23) Determine the variances in the following cases:

	Estimated cost	Actual cost
Direct labour costs	£500	£580
Direct material costs	£1400	£1250
Machine hours	800	780

(24) Define cutting speed, stating the units conventionally used, and state the relationship between it and tool life.

(25) What is the cutting speed for a 12 mm diameter drill rotating at 500 revolutions per minute?

(26) In a turning operation a 50 mm diameter bar is to be cut at a speed of 20 m/min. At how many revolutions per minute should the workpiece be rotated?

(27) At how many revolutions per minute should a component be milled when a 100 mm dia plain milling cutter is used and the required cutting speed is 25 m/min?

(28) What is the tool life for a tool being used at a cutting speed of 12 m/min if, for the operation, $C = 8.0$ and $n = 0.25$.

(29) For an operation where $n = 0.20$, by what percentage should the cutting speed be reduced to double the tool life?

(30) If $n = 0.20$ and $C = 50$, what cutting speed would be required to give a tool life of 1 hour?

(31) For an operation where $n = 0.15$ what will be the effect on the tooling cost of (a) doubling the tool life, (b) doubling the cutting speed?

(32) If the machining time for a component is 15 minutes, how many components can be machined at a cutting speed of 20 m/min between tool regrinds if $C = 100$ and $n = 0.20$?

(33) For the following operation what is the cost of machining 100 components at a cutting speed of 20 m/min? Ignore work-piece handling times, setting times and tool depreciation.
Machining time per component = 6 minutes
Time taken to change tool = 4 minutes
Time taken to regrind tool = 6 minutes
Machining cost = £0.10 per minute
$n = 0.20$; $C = 80$

(34) What is the most economical cutting speed for a machining operation where the cost of operating the machine is £20 per hour, the cost of a tool change is £5, $C = 80$ and $n = 0.20$?

(35) What is the most economical cutting speed for a machining operation where the cost of operating the machine is £12 per hour, the cost of a tool change is £5, $C = 120$ and $n = 0.25$?

(36) If, for the situation described in question 35, the machining cost were to be increased by 50% to £18, how would the most economical cutting speed change?

(37) Estimate the standard time to drill a hole 16 mm dia and 20 mm deep with a cutting speed of 15 m/min and a feed rate of 0.16 mm/rev.

(38) What is the cost of machining 100 holes 16 mm dia and 20 mm deep with a cutting speed of 15 m/min and a feed rate of 0.16 mm/rev if $n = 0.20$, $C = 50$, machining cost is £0.30 per minute, the handling time for the workpiece between drilling is 1 min, the time taken to change the tool is 1 min and the time taken to regrind the tool is 8 min? Ignore setting times and tool depreciation.

(39) An article in the Financial Times of December 7 1983, under the heading 'Where sputter means longer life' by I. Rodger, states 'The life of metal cutting tools can be increased by up to 10 times with a new process for applying titanium nitride coatings to them'. It also states it is 'expected many users would take advantage of the coating to improve productivity by increased cutting speeds'. Prepare a report on the implications of such an increase in tool life, commenting on cost factors, increased productivity and most economical cutting speeds.

2 Forming processes– metals

After working through this chapter you should be able to:

Appraise the type of product that may be produced by (a) casting processes, (b) manipulative processes, (c) powder techniques and (d) cutting, understanding the basic principles of the various processes.
Recognise the limitations and merits of the various processes.
Justify the selection of a particular process as viable in relation to quality, quantity and cost.

2.1 FORMING PROCESSES

With metals, the range of forming processes possible for component production can be divided into four main categories:

1 Casting This is the shaping of a material by pouring the liquid material into a mould.
2 Manipulative processes These involve shaping materials by plastic deformation methods.
3 Powder techniques This is the production of a shape by compacting a powder.
4 Cutting This is the production of a shape by metal removal.

In this chapter each of the above types of process will be considered in more detail so that comparisons can be made as to the suitability of a particular process for the manufacture of a component.

One factor that will be referred to is surface roughness. Roughness is defined as the irregularities in the surface texture which are inherent in the production process but excluding waviness and errors of form. Waviness may arise from such factors as machine or work deflections, vibrations, heat treatment or warping strains.

One measure of roughness is the arithmetical mean deviation, denoted by the symbol R_a. This is the arithmetical average value of the departure of the profile above and below the reference line throughout the prescribed sampling length. The reference line may be the centre line, this being a line chosen so that the sum of the areas contained between it and those parts of the surface profile which lie on either side of it are equal (*Figure 2.1*).

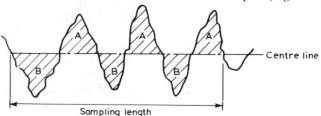

Figure 2.1 The centre line. The sum of the areas marked A equals the sum of those marked B

The following table indicates the significance of R_a values:

Surface texture	$R_a/\mu m$
Very rough	50
Rough	25
Semi rough	12.5
Medium	6.3
Semi fine	3.2
Fine	1.6
Coarse ground	0.8
Medium ground	0.4
Fine ground	0.2
Super fine	0.1

Another factor in making comparisons between processes is the tolerance possible. Tolerance is the difference between the maximum limit of size and the minimum limit of size. It is the amount by which deviation may occur from a desired dimension.

2.2 CASTING

Essentially, casting consists of pouring a liquid metal into a suitable mould and then permitting it to solidify, thereby producing a solid of the required shape. The products fall into two main categories, those for which the solid shape is just a convenient form for further processing, and those for which the component produced requires only some machining or finishing to give the final product.

Where the products are produced for further processing simple, regular geometrical shapes are generally used, the products being known as ingots, billets, pigs, slabs, or other descriptive terms. The shape adopted depends on the processes that are to follow.

Where the casting is used to produce the almost finished state product, a mould is used which has the internal shape and form of that required of the product. The mould has however to be designed in such a way that the liquid metal can easily and quickly flow to all parts. This has implications for the finished casting in that sharp corners and re-entrant sections have to be avoided and gradually tapered changes in section used. Account has also to be taken of the fact that the dimensions of the finished casting will be less than those of the mould due to shrinkage occurring when the metal cools from the liquid state to room temperature.

A number of casting methods are available, the choice of method depending on:
1 Size of casting required;
2 Number of castings required;
3 Complexity of the casting;
4 Mechanical properties required for the casting;
5 Surface finish required;
6 Dimensional accuracy required;
7 Metal to be used;
8 Cost per casting.

The casting methods available include:
1 Sand casting
This involves using a mould made of a mixture of sand and clay. The mixture is packed around a pattern of the required casting to

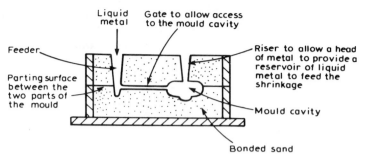

Figure 2.2 Sand casting

give the mould, which is usually made in two main parts so that the pattern can be extracted (*Figure 2.2*). The mould must be designed so that when the liquid metal is introduced into the mould, all air or gases can escape and the mould can be completely filled. After the casting has solidified the mould is broken open; the moulds only being used for the one casting. Some machining is always necessary with the casting, such as the trimming off of the metal in the feeder and riser.

Sand casting can be used for a wide range of casting sizes and for simple or complex shapes. Holes and inserts are possible. However, the mechanical properties, surface finish and dimensional accuracy of the casting are limited. Roughness values (R_a) of the order of 12.5 to 25 μm are produced. A wide range of alloys can be used. The cost of the mould is relatively cheap, at least in comparison with metal moulds, but the cost of the mould has to be defrayed against just one casting as it is broken up after being used only once. For small number production, sand casting is the cheapest casting process.

2 Die casting

This involves the use of a metal mould. With *gravity die casting* the liquid metal is poured into the mould, gravity being responsible for causing the metal to flow into all parts of the mould. With *pressure die casting* the liquid metal is injected into the mould under pressure. This enables the metal to be forced into all parts of the mould and enables very complex shapes with high dimensional accuracy to be produced.

There are limitations to the size of casting that can be produced with pressure die casting, the mass of the casting generally being less than about 5 kg. Gravity die casting can, however, be used for larger castings. Because of the metal mould is expensive, compared with, for example, a sand mould, this process is generally uneconomic for one-off castings or small runs. The mould can be used for many castings and thus the cost defrayed over the larger number of castings rather than just allocated to a few. The castings produced by this method have very good mechanical properties, dimensional accuracy and finish, good enough to reduce or even eliminate machining or other finishing processes. Roughness values (R_a) of the order of 0.8 to 1.6 μm are produced. The metals used with this casting method are limited to aluminium, copper, magnesium and zinc alloys.

The main cost factor is the cost of the metal mould. If the cost per casting is to be reasonable, there needs to be a large number production with a particular mould. The metal mould does,

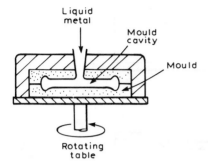

Figure 2.3 Centrifugal casting

however, mean that little further machining or finishing might be necessary and so reduces the cost element for such operations.

3 Centrifugal casting

This method involves either consumable or metal moulds, using the forces set up during rotation of the mould to force the liquid metal to cling to the inside of the rotating mould (*Figure 2.3*). This enables hollow objects to be produced without the use of an inner core in the mould. This method is used for simple geometrical shapes, e.g. large diameter pipes.

4 Investment casting

This method, sometimes known as *lost wax casting*, can be used with metals that have to withstand very high temperatures and so have high melting points, and for which high dimensional accuracy is required—aero engine blades are a typical product.

With this method the required shape is made from wax or a similar material. The wax pattern is then coated with a ceramic paste. When this coated wax pattern is heated the ceramic hardens, the wax melts and runs out to leave a mould cavity. The hot mould then has the liquid metal injected into it. After cooling the ceramic is broken away to leave the casting.

The size of casting that can be produced by this method is not as great as that possible with sand casting. The method does however give high dimensional accuracy and a good surface finish. Roughness values (R_a) of the order of 1.6 to 3.2 μm are produced. For large number production it is a more expensive method than die casting but is a cheaper method for small number production.

Choosing a casting process

The following factors largely determine the type of casting process used:

1 Large, heavy, casting Sand casting can be used for very large castings.

2 Complex design Sand casting is the most flexible method and can be used for very complex castings.

3 Thin walls Investment casting or pressure die casting can cope with walls as thin as 1 mm. Sand casting cannot cope with such thin walls.

4 Small castings Investment casting or die casting. Sand casting is not suitable for very small castings.

5 Good reproduction of detail Pressure die casting or investment casting, sand casting being the worst.

6 Good surface finish Pressure die casting or investment casting, sand casting being the worst.

7 High melting point alloys Sand casting or investment casting.

8 Tooling cost This is highest with pressure die casting. Sand casting is cheapest. However with large number production the tooling costs for the metal mould can be defrayed over a large number of castings, whereas the cost of the mould for sand casting is the same no matter how many castings are made because a new mould is required for each casting.

Design considerations when using casting

Rounded corners, no abrupt changes in section, gradually sloping surfaces are all necessary with casting if there is to be a proper flow of metal and a complete filling up of the mould. During the casting gas bubbles escape from the liquid metal and corners in which the

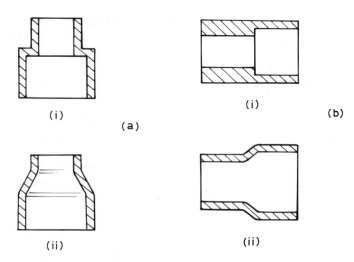

Figure 2.4 (a) The need for no sharp corners in casting means (ii) is preferred to (i) (b) The need for uniform thickness sections in casting means (ii) is preferred to (i)

gas could collect have to be eliminated. Thus for example in *Figure 2.4(a)* the design in (ii) is to be preferred to that in i).

Shrinkage occurs during the cooling and solidification of a casting. The amount of shrinkage depends on the metal being used and so the pattern used for the casting must be designed to take this into account, the pattern being larger than the required casting by an amount depending on the metal concerned. During the solidification the outer surfaces of the metal cool more rapidly than the inside of the metal. This can result in the outer layers solidifying while the inside is still liquid. When this liquid then contracts and solidifies, cavities can be caused if the solidifying inner liquid metal cannot pull in the outer solidified metal. The production of cavities due to this is markedly increased where the section thickness shows abrupt changes. Ideally a uniform thickness section should be used, however if this is not feasible a gradual change in thickness should occur rather than an abrupt change, *Figure 2.4(b)*.

When to use casting

The circumstances under which casting is likely to be the optimum method for product production is when:

1 The part has a large internal cavity. There would be a considerable amount of metal to be removed if machining were used, casting removing this need.

2 The part has a complex internal cavity. Machining might be impossible, by casting however very complex internal cavities can be produced.

3 The part is made of a material which is difficult to machine.

4 The metal used is expensive and so there is to be little waste.

5 The directional properties of a material are to be minimized. Metals subject to a manipulative process often have properties which differ in different directions.

6 The component has a complex shape. Casting may be more economical than assembling a number of individual parts.

Casting is not likely to be the optimum method for parts that are simple enough to be extruded or deep drawn.

2.3 MANIPULATIVE PROCESSES

Manipulative processes involve the shaping of a material by means of plastic deformation processes. Where the deformation takes place at a temperature in excess of the recrystallisation temperature of the metal the process is said to be *hot working*. Where the deformation is at a temperature below the recrystallisation temperature the process is said to be *cold working*.

When compared with hot working, cold working has the following advantages:

1 Better surface finish is produced.
2 Improved strength.
3 Better dimensional control.
4 Better reproducibility.
5 Directional properties can be imparted to the material.
6 Contamination is minimized.
7 No heating is required.

Cold working has however the following disadvantages when compared with hot working:

1 Higher forces are needed for plastic deformation.
2 More energy is needed for plastic deformation.
3 Work hardening occurs.
4 The resulting material has less ductility and toughness.
5 The directional properties given to the material may be detrimental.
6 The metal used must be clean and scale free.

Hot working

The main hot-working processes are rolling, forging and extruding. The following notes involve a closer look at these and related processes.

1 Rolling

This is the shaping of the metal by it being passed, hot, between rollers. With nominally parallel cylinder rolls, flat sheet or strip can be produced in long lengths. If contoured rollers are used, channel sections, rails, etc can be produced.

Hot rolling is usually done in a number of stages. This could be either a series of passes through one set of rollers or a continuous process with the material passing through a sequence of sets of rollers. *Figure 2.5(a)* shows the type of rolling sequence that is adopted in rolling a structural beam section.

Darlington and Simpson Rolling Mills Ltd in their catalogue state that over six hundred different rolled shapes are available, ranging from 1 kg to 10 kg per metre length. *Figure 2.5(b)* shows some of their rolled sections. Roughness values (R_a) of the order of 12.5 to 25 μm are produced.

2 Forging

Forging is a squeezing process, the hot metal being squeezed by pressing or hammering between a pair of dies. *Heavy smith's forging* or *open die forging* involves the metal being hammered by a vertically moving tool against a stationary tool, or anvil. Such

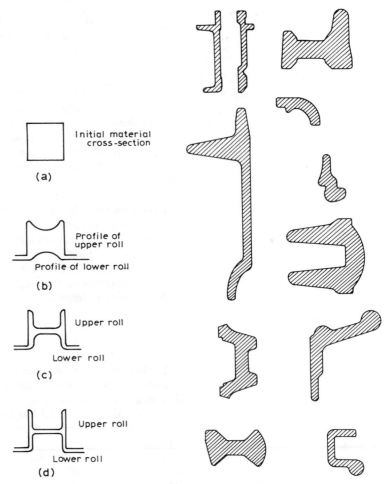

Figure 2.5 (a) The type of rolling sequence used for a structural beam section (b), (c), (d) Examples of rolled sections

forgings are fairly crude in form and generally are only the first stage in the forming operation. *Closed die forging* involves the hot metal being squeezed between two shaped dies which effectively form a complete mould (*Figure 2.6*). The metal in the cavity is squeezed under pressure in the cavity, flowing under the pressure and filling the cavity. In order to completely fill the cavity a small excess of metal is allowed and this is squeezed outwards to form a flash which is later trimmed away. *Drop forging* is one form of closed die forging and uses the impact of a hammer to cause the metal billet to flow and fill the die cavity. The term *machine forging* (or *press forging*) is used for the closed die forging process where a press is used to slowly squeeze the metal billet between the dies.

The cost of forging is high for small number production because of the cost of the dies and large number production is necessary to reduce the die cost per unit product produced. For example, with an aluminium alloy being forged, increasing the production run from 100 units to 1000 units can result in the cost per unit decreasing by 50% to 75%. To give an indication of the factors, and their relative costings, involved in producing a forging the

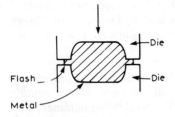

Figure 2.6 Closed die forging

following are the costs for a drop forging (Iron and Steel Institute, ISI publication No. 138, 1971):

	Percentage of total production cost
Material	52
Direct overheads	15
Direct labour	10
Dies	8
Maintenance	4
Stock heating	3
Other	8

Forging results in a product superior in toughness and impact strength to that given by casting. The process also results in the welding up of shrinkage cavities in the cast ingot used for the forging. The process can be used to give a fibre structure within the material, a directionality of properties, which minimises the chances of crack formation and enhances the properties in service of the product. Roughness values (R_a) of the order of 3.2 to 12.5 μm are produced.

There are few limits to the shape of component that can be forged with a closed die. However, webs and thin sections should not be made too thin because they are likely to cool too quickly and thus necessitate a greater forging pressure. Also corners should not have very small radii as larger radii allow a better metal flow during the forging operation.

The flash, see *Figure 2.6*, that is produced with forging has to be machined off, so to that extent some machining is always necessary after forging.

3 Extrusions

With hot extrusion, the hot metal is forced under pressure to flow through a die, i.e. a shaped orifice. Two basic methods of hot extrusion are used, *direct extrusion* and *indirect extrusion*. *Figure 2.7* shows the fundamentals of these two methods. Rods are formed by extruding the billet material through a die and give a solid product of uniform cross-section. Tubes and other hollow shapes can be extruded by using an internal mandrel (*Figure 2.8(a)*) or a spider mandrel (*Figure 2.8(b)*). As the material flows past the spider a further reduction between the die and the mandrel forces the material to close up and weld together.

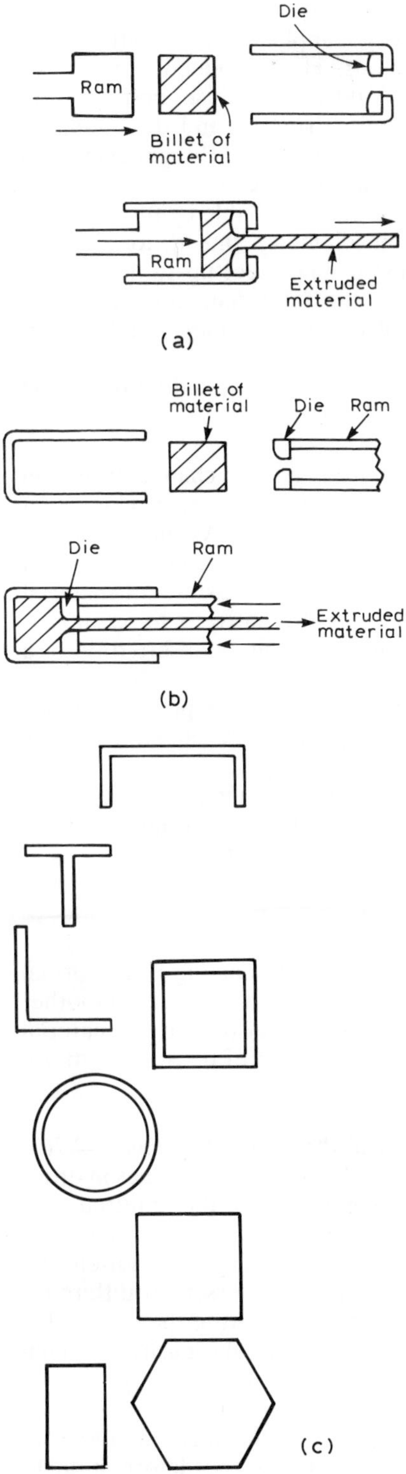

Figure 2.7 (a) Direct extrusion
(b) Indirect extrusion
(c) Some of the standard sections available with extrusion, considerably more complex sections are possible

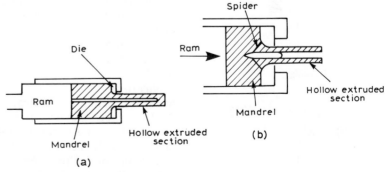

Figure 2.8 Extruding hollow sections

The process is used extensively with aluminium, copper and magnesium alloys to produce very complex shaped sections and with steel for less complex sections. High production rates are possible and the products have a good surface finish, better tensile strength and more favourable grain structure and directionality than the starting material used for the extrusion. Roughness values (R_a) of the order of 0.8 to 3.2 μm are produced.

To illustrate the types of product sizes available by this method, aluminium tubes up to 150 mm in diameter and up to 2500 mm long have been produced; tubes in mild steel up to 130 mm in diameter and 750 mm long. Minimum tube diameters are about 5 mm. Aluminium cans up to 350 mm in diameter and 1500 mm long are possible.

Extrusion dies are expensive and thus large quantity production is necessary so that the cost can be spread.

4 Upsetting

There are many products that require a marked change of section along their length. One possibility is to machine the product from material having the largest diameter required. As the volume of material at the largest diameter may be small in comparison with the rest of the product this can be extremely wasteful of material and involve high machining costs. An alternative is to use upsetting. In this process a billet or extrusion is inserted into a stationary die with part of it protruding from the die (*Figure 2.9*). A punch moving along the die axis impacts on the protruding part and 'squashes' it out to the required diameter. A second blow may be used to complete the head shape.

The process is used for high volume fastener production, e.g. rivets and bolts. Hot upsetting is used for those materials that have low ductility in the cold. Otherwise cold upsetting is used.

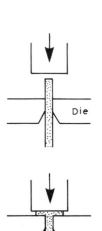

Figure 2.9 Upsetting

Cold working   The main cold working processes are:

1 Cold rolling

Cold rolling is the shaping of a material by passing it, at normal temperatures, between rollers. This gives a cleaner, smoother finish to the metal surface than rolling hot, also a harder material is produced. Roughness values of the order of 0.4 to 3.2 μm are produced.

2 Wire drawing

This involves the pulling of material through a die (*Figure 2.10*). Wire manufacture can involve a number of drawing stages in order that the initial material can be brought down to the required size. As this cold working hardens the material there may be annealing operations between the various drawing stages to soften the material and so permit further drawing. The essential difference between drawing and extrusion is that in drawing the material is pulled through the die, in extrusion the material is pushed through the die.

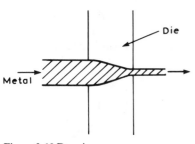

Figure 2.10 Drawing

3 Shearing

Shearing, bending and deep drawing are the three methods of working sheet metal in presses. Shearing is the deformation to shear failure of a metal in order to cut various shapes from the metal sheet. It is cutting without the formation of chips or the use of burning or melting. *Figure 2.11* illustrates the basic shearing process, the punch descending onto the metal sheet and deforming

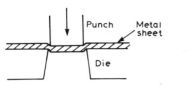

Figure 2.11 The basic shearing process

it plastically into the die. The punch penetrates into the metal, the opposite surface of the metal bulging and flowing into the die. When the punch has penetrated a certain distance into the metal, the applied stress exceeds the shear strength of the metal and the metal suddenly shears through the remainder of the thickness. The depth of penetration that occurs before the metal shears depends on the ductility and shear strength of the material. Thus for annealed mild steel the depth of penetration is of the order of 50% of the sheet thickness, for partially cold worked mild steel this percentage penetration drops to of the order of 40%. On the metal pressed out of the sheet the depth of penetration can be seen as a polished area on the cut surface (*Figure 2.12*).

The amount of the clearance between the punch and the die (*Figure 2.13*) also affects the appearance of the cut surface. If an adequate clearance is used the cut edges may be sufficiently smooth for use without further finishing. An adequate clearance is generally of the order of 5% tto 10% of the sheet thickness. *Figure 2.12* shows the slightly tapered form of the cut surface when there is adequate clearance and *Figure 2.14* shows the type of surface produced when there is inadequate clearance. This occurs because the cracks developed in the sheet during the deformation do not all run together to produce a clean break when the clearance is inadequate but do when the clearance is adequate.

Piercing and *blanking* are shearing operations. With piercing the piece removed from the sheet or strip is the waste item and the perforated strip or sheet is the required product. With blanking, the piece removed from the sheet or strip is the required product and the perforated strip or sheet is the waste item. In some cases a combination of piercing and blanking may be necessary, this often being accomplished with a single stroke of the punch. An example of a product requiring both piercing and blanking is the simple washer—the piercing being needed for the central hole and the blanking to produce the outer circular cut and so the completed washer (*Figure 2.15*).

A number of other operations are likely to have taken place before piercing or blanking occurs. Thus the material may have

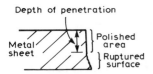

Figure 2.12 Penetration during shearing

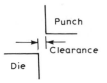

Figure 2.13 Clearance

Figure 2.14 The cut surface with inadequate clearance

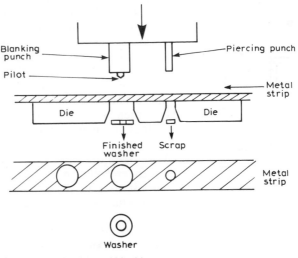

Figure 2.15 Piercing and blanking

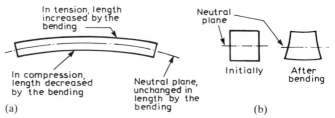

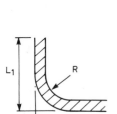

Figure 2.16 Bending. (a) Effect on section. (b) Effect on cross-section

Figure 2.17 Length of blank = $L_1 + L_2 - D$, where D is the allowance

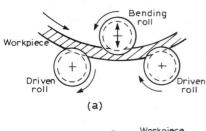

(a)

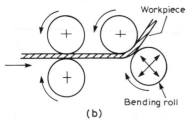

(b)

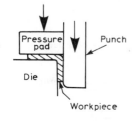

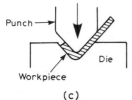

(c)

Figure 2.18 (a) Three-roll bending
(b) Four-roll bending
(c) Bending by means of press-tools

been taken from a coil and has to be cut to length and also flattened. This generally takes place by the rolled sheet being fed between rollers, to straighten it, and then sheared to give strip of the right length.

4 Bending

When a bar, tube, strip or wire is bent on one side of the neutral plane there are tensile stresses and on the other side compressive stresses (*Figure 2.16*). When these stresses are made high enough plastic deformation can occur, in both tension and compression. A problem, however, in bending a piece of material to a particular curvature is that when the bending force has been removed the material has the tendency to *spring back* and so adopt a different curvature. One method for compensating for this spring back is to overbend slightly.

When a piece of metal is stretched and becomes longer, it suffers a reduction in its width. Similarly, when a piece of material is compressed and becomes shorter, it suffers an increase in width. When bending occurs, there is a reduction in the width on the tensile side of the neutral plane and an increase in width on the compression side. Thus an initially rectangular cross-section is no longer rectangular (*Figure 2.16*).

One effect of the above change in cross-section is that the neutral axis becomes displaced towards the compressed side of a bend. This affects the calculations that a designer needs to make in determining the length of a blank necessary to produce a bent part of given dimensions. An allowance has to be made for the neutral axis shift, the allowance depending on the thickness of the blank and the bend radius. Tables are available for the allowances. As an example, the length of the blank required for the bend shown in *Figure 2.17* is $L_1 + L_2 - D$, where D is the allowance. If the blank had a thickness t then if the radius of the bend R equals t then $D = 1.7t$, if $R = 2t$ then $D = 2.0t$.

Figure 2.18 illustrates several ways of bending materials. Many products can be made by the relatively simple process of bending, e.g. such commonplace items as paper clips, links, hooks, clips, springs and many items used in electrical fitments.

5 Deep drawing

With deep drawing, sheet metal is pushed into an aperture by a punch and cup-shaped articles produced. This process had its earliest uses in the production of artillery shells and cartridge cases. Ductile materials, e.g. aluminium, brass, mild steel, must be used.

Figure 2.19 illustrates the sequence of events for a deep drawing operation. An important point to note for this process is that the edges of the blank are not clamped. Thus as the blank is pushed

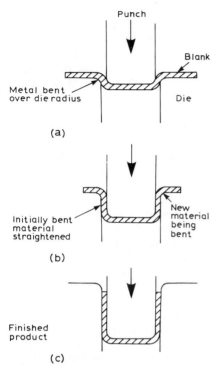

Figure 2.19 Deep drawing

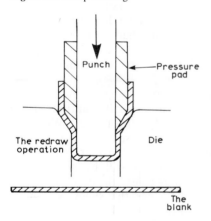

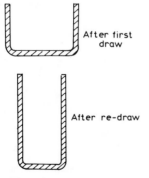

Figure 2.21 The redraw process

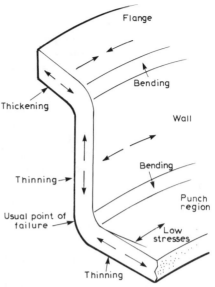

Figure 2.20 Stresses during deep drawing

into the aperture, the edges of the sheet move, when the punch first impacts on the blank, the blank is bent over the edges of the die. As the die continues to move downwards, the previously bent material is straightened against the wall of the die to create the cylindrical side walls of the cup-shaped object. New material is bent over the edge of the die, this material resulting from the movement towards the punch of the edges of the blank. This process of straightening the previously bent material and bending new material continues until the finished product is produced, often when all the blank material has been pulled into the die.

Figure 2.20 shows the types of stresses experienced by the material during deep drawing. The flange material is subject to tensile stress in the axial direction but compressive stress in the circumferential direction. This is because the circumference of the blank is being reduced as it is pushed into the die. The result of this is a thinning of the flange material and a tendency for the material to wrinkle in order to accommodate the change in circumference. For this reason a pressure pad is generally pressed against the flange during the drawing. As the material in the flange passes over the edge of the die it is bent. The wall is subject to vertical and circumferential tensile stresses. The effect of these stresses is to cause the material to thin. Under the base of the punch the material is subject to tensile stresses.

In deep drawing, the region of thinnest material is close to the initial bending region at the punch edge. It is here that failure is most likely to occur. Thus the thickness at this region may be 90% of the original blank thickness, whereas in the flange close to the die edge it may be 115%.

In some circumstances more than one drawing operation may be used in order to achieve the final required product shape. Sometimes the material may be annealed between drawing operations to maintain ductility. *Figure 2.21* shows the method adopted for a *redrawing process*.

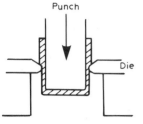

Figure 2.22 Ironing

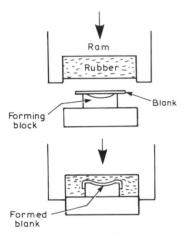

Figure 2.23 Forming with rubber

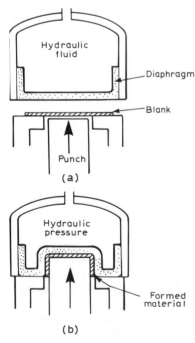

Figure 2.24 Flexible die forming. (a) Initial position. (b) Material being formed

Deep drawing is not only used to produce cup-like objects but it is also a very widely used process for the shaping of sheet metal. Examples are the production of steel kitchen sink tops and car body pieces. Whether, in all cases, the term 'deep' is appropriate for the drawing operation is irrelevant because the basic principles are the same. The term *pressing* is sometimes used for the operation, because the drawing is carried out using a press.

6 Ironing

The length of a drawn cup can be extended by thinning the cup walls with an ironing process. The cup wall is squeezed between a punch and the die, the initial wall thickness being greater than the clearance between the punch and the die (*Figure 2.22*).

7 Forming with rubber or fluid pressure

With the deep drawing process described in the previous section rigid metal dies were used with rigid metal punches. Such press tools can be used to produce many thousands of components, but the cost of such tools can be high. Where small production runs are required, the tooling cost may make the production uneconomic. With smaller production runs, i.e. a thousand or less, a flexible die may be a cheaper and more economic alternative.

Rubber, in a confined space, when acted on by a pressure behaves rather like a fluid and transmits the pressure uniformly in all directions. *Figure 2.23* shows how this principle is utilised in a forming process. The metal blank is placed over a forming block. Then a ram presses a rubber pad over the blank and block. The pressure transmitted through the rubber presses the blank over the forming block. The forming blocks can be made of wood and thus are cheaper to produce than conventional metal dies. The process is used for multiple-axis bending and some shallow drawing.

Another flexible die method involves the use of a fluid with a diaphragm *Figure 2.24* shows one form of such an arrangement.

8 Stretch forming

This process was developed to enable sheet metal parts, particularly large sheets, to be formed economically in small quantities. The metal sheet, while in tension, is wrapped over a former. With no stretching forces a bent sheet will have tensile stress on the surface of the sheet, for which the bending causes the material to be extended. On the other surface the sheet will be subject to compressive stress, for which the bending causes the material to be compressed (see *Figure 2.25*). If however the sheet is under tension when bent, all the stresses in the material may be tensile, as the entire material has been extended in comparison with its non-bent and non-stretched length. *Figure 2.25* shows the stretch

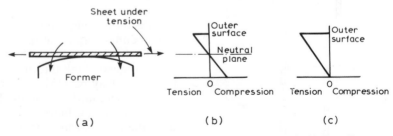

Figure 2.25 Stretch forming. (a) The stretch forming process. (b), (c) The effect on the stresses in the bent material

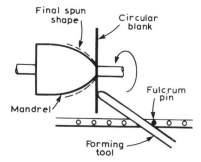

Figure 2.26 Spinning with a hand-held tool

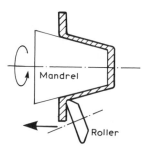

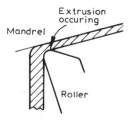

Figure 2.27 Flow turning

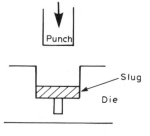

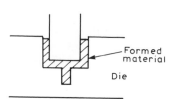

Figure 2.28 Impact extrusion

forming process and the stress distribution throughout the thickness of a sheet when bent without stretching and then with stretching.

When a sheet is bent, without being stretched, the surface that is in compression is prone to buckle or distort. If, however, the material is stretched when bent this distortion can be avoided.

9 Spinning

Spinning can be used for the production of circular shaped objects. A circular blank is rotated and then pressure applied to it by means of a forming tool in order to bend the blank into the required shape (*Figure 2.26*). This is an economic method for small numbers of components or for large components where other forming methods would involve high costs. Aluminium, brass and mild steel are examples of materials formed by this process. A typical type of product is a metal reflector.

A variation of spinning is called *flow turning*. Instead of a forming tool being just pressed against the blank to cause it to become bent to the required shape, a roller is used (*Figure 2.27*). This not only forms the blank to the shape of the mandrel but also progressively extrudes it. The wall thickness of the formed product is thus less than the initial thickness of the blank. Both the shape of the product and its thickness are thus under control, unlike spinning where only the shape is controlled.

10 Impact extrusion

This process involves a punch hitting a slug of the material which is held in a die (*Figure 2.28*). The impact causes the slug material to flow up the space between the punch and the walls of the die.

Impact extrusion is widely used with the softer materials, i.e. zinc, lead and aluminium, and is used for the production of collapsible tubes or cans, e.g. zinc dry battery cases and toothpaste tubes. A small deep can in these materials can be more easily produced by this method than by deep drawing.

11 Explosive forming

Explosive forming is an example of a relatively new group of forming processes, known as *high velocity metal forming*. *Figure 2.29* illustrates the basic principle. An explosive charge is detonated under water and the resulting pressure wave used to press a metal blank against the die. This method can be used with a wide variety of materials, including some of the high strength materials which may be difficult to form by other methods. Complex parts can be produced at one 'blow'. Large reflectors, cylinders, domes, etc. can be produced.

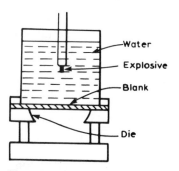

Figure 2.29 Explosive forming

12 Cold forging

Impact extrusion is often combined with other operations such as upsetting, drawing, etc to convert the billet into the finished product. Because these operations are carried out at room temperature they are collectively known as cold forging.

High production rates can be achieved with the finished products having greater tensile strengths and more favourable grain flow than the starting material. Compared with machining processes there is little waste material. Generally, there is little if any finish machining required as a good surface finish is produced. The process is used for the production of solid objects with differently shaped heads and stepped shafts, hollow objects open at both ends with stepped internal and external diameters, hollow articles with internal and external splines or teeth, etc.

Press capacity

Shearing, bending and drawing are all processes which can use presses. In selecting a press consideration has to be given to the required press capacity for the process concerned. The press capacity, or size, depends on:

1 The force required.
2 The length of the press stroke required.
3 If a drawing operation, the depth of draw required.
4 The number of press strokes per minute required.
5 The size of press bed needed.
6 The methods and direction of the blank feed.

In shearing the maximum punch force required depends on the edge area to be sheared and the shear strength τ of the material.

$$\text{Maximum punch force} = \tau \times \text{area}$$
$$= \tau \times \text{material thickness} \times \text{work profile perimeter}$$

Hence the maximum force required to blank a circle of radius 30 mm from a steel sheet of thickness 2.0 mm and having a shear strength of 430 MPa (or MN m^{-2}) is

$$\text{Maximum force} = (430 \times 10^6) \times (2.0 \times 10^{-3}) \times (2\pi \times 30 \times 10^{-3})$$
$$= 1.62 \times 10^5 \text{ N (or } 0.162 \text{ MN)}$$

Figure 2.30 shows how, during shearing, the punch force varies with the penetration into the sheet when normal clearances are used. To a reasonable approximation the work done is the product of the maximum punch force F_{max} and the distance the punch penetrates into the sheet before rupture occurs. But this distance is equal to the percentage penetration multiplied by the sheet thickness.

$$\text{Work done} = F_{max} \times (\% \text{ penetration}) \times (\text{sheet thickness})$$

Thus in the example given above, if the penetration was 30% then the work done would be

$$\text{work done} = (1.62 \times 10^5) \times (30/100) \times (2.0 \times 10^{-3})$$
$$= 97.2 \text{ J}$$

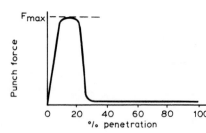

Figure 2.30 Forces during shearing. The area under the graph is the work done

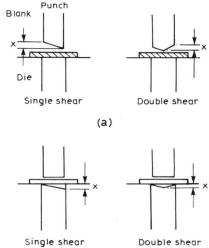

Single shear   Double shear

(a)

Single shear   Double shear

(b)

Figure 2.31 (a) Shear on the punch (b) Shear on the die. The amount of shear has been exaggerated, **x** is less than the blank thickness

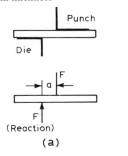

(a)

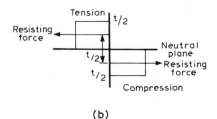

(b)

Figure 2.32 (a) Bending moment on sheet (b) Stress distribution across section

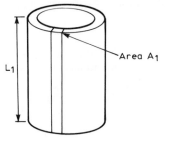

Figure 2.33 A strip on a drawn cup wall

This work may be spread over a larger length of the press stroke by putting *shear* on the punch or the die. This is particularly useful if the blank is of substantial thickness. *Figure 2.31(a)* illustrates the form of single and double shear on the punch. This type of shear tends to be used when piercing or cropping so that only the punched out slug is deformed. *Figure 2.3(b)* shows the shear applied to the die. This is used when blanking, to give a flat blank.

In using a press for bending, as in *Figure 2.18(c)*, the bending moment is given by (*Figure 2.32*)

$$\text{bending moment} = Fa$$

where F is the punch load and a the clearance, i.e. the distance between the edge of the punch and the side of the die. This clearance is however virtually the same as the sheet thickness t. Hence

$$\text{bending moment} = Ft$$

Because the entire section of the sheet is to be plastically deformed it must all reach the yield stress and so the stress distribution across the bent section is likely to be something like that shown in *Figure 2.32*. Hence, to a reasonable approximation, the moment of resistance to the bending is given by

$$\begin{aligned}\text{moment of resistance} &= (\text{resisting force}) \times \tfrac{1}{2}t \\ &= (\sigma_y \times b \times \tfrac{1}{2}t) \times \tfrac{1}{2}t \\ &= \tfrac{1}{4}bt^2\sigma_y\end{aligned}$$

where σ_y is the yield stress and b the breadth of the sheet. Hence

$$Ft = \tfrac{1}{4}bt^2\sigma_y$$
$$F = \tfrac{1}{4}bt\sigma_y$$

Thus for a bend in mild steel, with a yield stress of 200 MPa, sheet of thickness 3.0 mm and width 20 mm, the force needed is about

$$\text{force} = \tfrac{1}{4} \times (20 \times 10^{-3}) \times (3.0 \times 10^{-3}) \times 200 \times 10^{-6}$$
$$= 3000\,\text{N} \ (3.0\,\text{kN})$$

With deep drawing, as in *Figure 2.19*, one way of considering the punch force required is to consider a vertical strip of the drawn cup wall (*Figure 2.33*). The effect of the drawing has been to take a piece of the original blank material, length L_0 and cross-sectional area A_0, and stretch it so that it has an extended length of L_1 and a cross-sectional area of A_1. The punch in producing this extension has applied a force of F through the distance L_1. Hence the work done by the punch is FL_1.

$$\text{Work done by punch} = FL_1$$

If the stress-strain graph for the material, a ductile material, can be considered to be given by *Figure 2.34* then the energy needed per

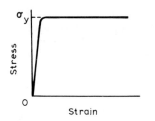

Figure 2.34 The idealised stress-strain graph

unit volume to extend the material is the area under the stress-strain graph and to a reasonable approximation this is

energy per unit volume = yield stress × strain

But the strain = $(L_1 - L_0)/L_0$, hence

$$\text{energy per unit volume} = \sigma_y = \frac{(L_1 - L_0)}{L_0}$$

The volume of the material is unchanged during the drawing and thus

$$A_0 L_0 = A_1 L_1$$

Hence   energy $= A_1 L_1 \times \sigma_y \times \dfrac{(L_1 - L_0)}{L_0}$

and so $FL_1 = A_1 L_1 \times \sigma_y \times \dfrac{(L_1 - L_1)}{L_0}$

$$F = A_1 \sigma_y \left(\frac{L_1}{L_0} - 1\right)$$

and as $A_0/A_1 = L_1/L_0$

$$F = A_1 \sigma_y \left(\frac{A_0}{A_1} - 1\right)$$

If a circular blank of diameter D and thickness t is used to produce a cup of diameter d and with the material thickness unchanged at t, then

initial cross-sectional area = circumference × t

Hence $A_0 = \pi D t$

The new cross-sectional area is

$$A_1 = \pi d t$$

Hence $F = \pi d t \sigma_y \left(\dfrac{D}{d} - 1\right)$

The ratio D/d is known as the drawing ratio. The maximum value of this ratio likely to be achieved in practice is about 2.0. Hence the maximum drawing force is when this ratio occurs, i.e. when

$$F = \pi d t \sigma_y$$

Thus if a cup of diameter 50 mm is to be drawn from a blank of diameter 100 mm and sheet of thickness 2.0 mm and having a yield stress of 200 MPa, then the force required is

$$F = \pi \times (50 \times 10^{-3}) \times (2.0 \times 10^{-3}) \times (200 \times 10^{-6}) \times \left(\frac{100}{50} - 1\right)$$

$$= 6.28 \times 10^4 \, \text{N} \; (62.8 \, \text{kN})$$

All the calculations in this section have made approximations. They have also ignored frictional effects. Thus in the case of the deep drawing an allowance for friction between the cup and the die walls might increase the required force by 30%.

Types of press

There are several types of press, the main two types being fly-presses and powered presses.

Fly presses are hand powered machines. The operator rotates a horizontal lever, weighted at its ends, to transfer energy to the rotating lever and thence via a screw mechanism to the ram. The tool, or punch, fits into the lower end of the ram. Limited amounts of energy are available by this method. The force is limited and, for this reason, the use of fly presses is restricted to blanking, piercing, bending and forming of small thickness material where only small forces are required.

Power presses are electrically driven. An electric motor is used to store energy in a flywheel; the energy being subsequently taken from the flywheel to activate the ram. Power presses can generate large amounts of energy and produce large forces. Hence the limitations to the work that can be handled is determined only by the size of the machine.

Compared with fly presses, power presses are expensive, not only in initial capital cost but also in tooling cost. The speed of a power press is, however, greater than that of a fly press and continuous production is possible.

Combination and progression press tools

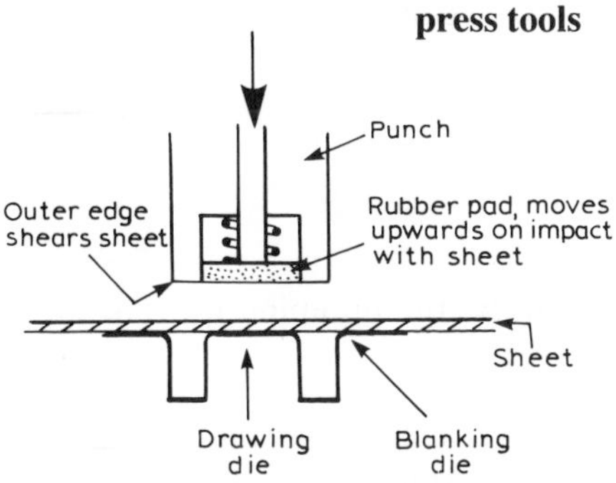

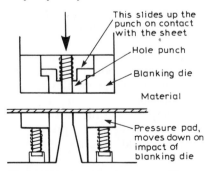

Figure 2.35 A combination press tool for a cup shaped object

Figure 2.36 A combination press tool for a washer

In a single-stage operation the press tool is used to carry out one operation—blanking. However it is often possible to incorporate two or more operations into one tool so that the tool is used to carry out these operations in combination. Thus the *combination tool* may blank and draw in the one stroke of the ram. *Figure 2.35* illustrates this.

Another type of combination tool is used for the forming of washers. The sheet is both blanked and pierced. *Figure 2.36* illustrates this. With combination tools the increased cost of the tooling is generally more than offset by the increased production rate, provided that large production runs are required.

With a combination tool the various punches and dies are incorporated on the same axis, a *progression tool* however has more than one press operation but they are placed at different positions along the tool. *Figure 2.15* shows the production of a washer by progressive piercing and blanking. As the strip material progresses through the tool, the piercing punch cuts the hole for the centre of the washer. This part of the strip then progresses to the blanking punch which cuts the outer edge of the washer and so the complete washer is produced. The sequence is a continuous operation with both punches being operated by the same stroke of the ram. The strip of material is thus progressivly worked on as it is fed through the tool.

Progression tools have the advantage over combination tools that damage to any one punch or die does not mean the replacement of the entire set. However, combination tools are preferable if accurate alignment is required for the various operations. Progression tools are usually cheaper than combination tools.

Progression tools may incorporate a combination tool at one station.

When combination or progression tools are used, the capacity of the press has to be greater than for a single operation. The following calculation illustrates this.

The maximum force required to blank a circle of radius 30 mm from a steel sheet of thickness 2.0 mm and having a shear strength of 430 MPa (or MN m^{-2}) is given by (as earlier in this chapter):

$$\text{Maximum punch force} = \tau \times \text{material thickness} \times \text{work profile}$$
$$\text{perimeter}$$
$$= (430 \times 10^6) \times (2.0 \times 10^{-3}) \times (2\pi \times 20 \times 10^{-3})$$
$$= 1.62 \times 10^5 \, \text{N}$$

The maximum force required to pierce a hole of radius 20 mm from the above sheet is given by:

$$\text{Maximum punch force} = (430 \times 10^6) \times (2.0 \times 10^{-3}) \times (2\pi \times 20 \times 10^{-3})$$
$$= 1.08 \times 10^5 \, \text{N}$$

If single stage operations are used for the production of a washer in the above material with an external radius of 30 mm and an internal radius of 20 mm, the maximum punch force required is:

$$1.62 \times 10^5 \, \text{N}$$

The maximum punch force required if a combination or a progressive tool is used is

$$1.62 \times 10^5 + 1.08 \times 10^5 = 2.70 \times 10^5 \, \text{N}$$

When to use manipulative processes

Manipulative processes are likely to be the optimum method for product production when:

1. The part is to be formed from sheet metal. Depending on the form required, shearing, bending or drawing may be appropriate if the components are not too large.
2. Long lengths of constant cross-section are required. Extrusion or rolling would be the optimum methods in that long lengths of quite complex cross-section can be produced without any need for machining.
3. The part has no internal cavities. Forging might be used, particularly if better toughness and impact strength is required than is obtainable with casting. Also directional properties can be imparted to the material to improve its performance in service.
4. Directional properties have to be imparted to the part.
5. Seamless cup-shaped objects or cans have to be produced. Deep drawing or impact extrusion would be the optimum methods.
6. The component is to be made from material in wire or bar form. Bending or upsetting can be used.

2.4 POWDER TECHNIQUE

This process is essentially the production of the required shape by pressing fine powders together and then heating them so that they bond together. This last part of the process is known as **sintering**. The various stages in the production can be summarised as follows.

1 Blending
This involves mixing the appropriate powder, or powders, with a lubricant. The purpose of the lubricant is to reduce friction between the grains of the powder when they are compacted, as well as to reduce die wear.

2 Compacting
The powder is placed in the die and subjected to pressure to compact it, pressures of the order of 100 to 400 MPa commonly being used (*Figure 2.37*). A variety of methods is used to apply this pressure, the method depending on the shape of the component being produced.

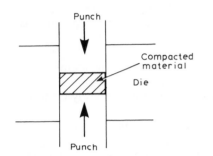

Figure 2.37 Compacting

3 Sintering
The particles in the shaped object are then bonded together by heating at a high temperature for a period of time; usually from half an hour to several hours. During this time the volatile lubricant materials are driven off. The temperature used is below the melting point of the metal powder, generally being about 70–80% of the melting temperature.

The process involves no waste materials and usually no machining is required; the product being the required shape and surface finish. The process can use materials which cannot be shaped by other methods, either because they have high melting points or are extremely brittle. Cobalt-bonded tungsten cutting tools are made this way, and the material is very difficult to form by any other process. Also products of complex shape that would require considerable machining can, with advantage, be manufactured in this way.

Components can be produced with a calculated amount of porosity. Thus, a filter might be made with fine pores about 0.002 mm dia., filling about 80% of the material. Porous bearings can be manufactured containing oil to give self-lubrication.

High rates of production are possible, and the operation does not involve highly skilled labour. The shaped dies and punches are expensive due to the use of expensive materials for the dies and punches. These materials are necessary because of the high pressures and the severe abrasion involved. A large number of components need to be made in order that the die and punch costs can be widely spread and not be too significant an element in the total product cost. This often means production runs in excess of 10 000 components.

In most cases the strength properties of the product are inferior to those that would be obtained using forging or casting techniques. Often, however, the materials that are used would present problems with other methods.

The process poses design restrictions regarding the shapes of the components that can be produced, if uniform density is required in the product. Without uniform density there cannot be uniform strength. Holes having axes perpendicular to the direction of the press force are not possible. Multiple stepped diameters, grooves and undercuts also present problems. The main types of components made by this method have an almost uniform cross-section throughout the length of the component.

2.5 CUTTING AND GRINDING

Some of the most common ways of cutting metals involve machine tools, the operations being known as **machining**. All such operations involve a tool being in contact with the workpiece, the machine moving one relative to the other. The operation results in the removal of unwanted metal from the workpiece, the pieces of unwanted material being known as chips (*Figure 2.38*).

The energy supplied to the tool during the cutting operation is used in four ways:

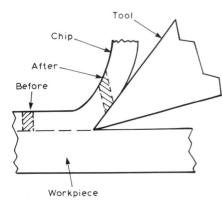

Figure 2.38 Machining

1 The energy used to break the bonding between the atoms of the metal and create new exposed surfaces;
2 The kinetic energy given to the chip as it moves away from the workpiece and the tool;
3 The energy required to slide the chip along the face of the tool, frictional forces having to be overcome;
4 The shear energy required in deforming the material, the shaded areas in *Figure 2.38* showing the shape of the material before and after cutting and the shearing action of the forces involved in cutting.

Most of the energy used in the cutting operation is involved in the shear energy required to deform the material, this often representing some 75% of the total energy. The other main element is the energy involved in sliding the chip along the face of the tool. The other energy terms are generally insignificant.

The outcome of this energy is, in the main, a rise in temperature of the workpiece. Very high temperatures can be produced, even where liquid coolants are used. During the machining it is the material of the workpiece that should be deformed while the tool remains rigid. This means that the tool material must be stronger than the workpiece material, especially at the high temperatures that can be reached at the tool-workpiece interface. Basically three types of tool materials are used—tool steels, metal carbides and ceramics.

Although the material of the workpiece must be deformable and less strong than the tool material, problems can arise if it is very ductile. Highly ductile materials are said to have poor machinability. This is because such materials produce a continuous chip and so there is a large area of material in contact with the face of the tool. This results in larger forces, and energy, being needed; also greater tool wear. Annealed pure metals are examples of such materials.

Less ductile materials are easier to machine, with the more brittle materials being the best. This is because the material produces only short chips, due to the fact that cracks are easily initiated and propagated in such materials. Grey cast iron has good machinability, this being as a result of the graphite flakes in the iron acting as crack initiators. Free cutting steels have had sulphur

Figure 2.39 Turning

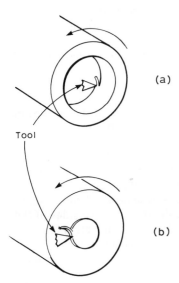

Figure 2.40 (a) Boring, (b) facing

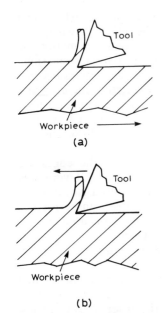

Figure 2.41 (a) Planing, (b) shaping

added to them to produce manganese sulphide inclusions. During machining the manganese sulphide forms a lubricant film along the tool face which lowers the frictional force and hence the cutting force and energy required.

There are essentially five basic metal cutting processes—turning, planing, milling, drilling and grinding. In the following notes a brief look is taken at each of these processes and their general characteristics.

1 Turning

Figure 2.39 illustrates the type of cutting operation involved in turning. A single-point tool is used with a cylindrical workpiece, the tool being held stationary while the workpiece rotates. The product of a turning operation is always cylindrical. The surface roughness that can be expected is of the order of 0.4 to 6 µm (the R_a value), while minimum tolerances of the order of 0.0125 mm can be achieved.

The machine tool used for turning is the lathe. Other operations are also possible with the lathe. These include

boring, which involves the enlargement of an existing hole (*Figure 2.40a*);

facing, which is the production of a flat surface as the result of the tool being fed across the end of the rotating workpiece (*Figure 2.40b*)

drilling with the drill fed against the end of the rotating workpiece and screwcutting.

There are a number of types of lathe and the choice of lathe depends on a number of factors. One factor is the number of parts to be produced. The centre lathe is a versatile machine tool but is not ideal for rapid mass production because of the time required for changing and setting tools and making measurements on the workpiece. Also a skilled operator is required.

Turret and capstan lathes are more appropriate to mass production in that a number of tools can be set up on the machine and then brought into use as required without the need for further adjustments, tool changing or measurements. While a skilled operator is needed for the setting up a semi-skilled worker can be used for the operation. NC lathes permit even more automatic operation.

2 Planing and shaping

Planing is used to produce flat surfaces or slots. It involves a single-edge cutting tool (as does turning with a lathe) operating in the way illustrated in *Figure 2.41*, the tool being stationary while the workpiece moves. Shaping differs from planing in that the tool moves while the workpiece is stationary, otherwise the principle is the same.

Planers tend to be used for the larger scale jobs than shapers. However both machine tools are not too widely used because other machine tools, such as millers or grinders, can do the same job more economically if a large number of parts are to be machined. Shapers tend to be used to some extent in low volume production.

Both planing and shaping tend to give surface roughness values of about 0.8 to 15 µm and minimum tolerances of the order of 0.025 mm.

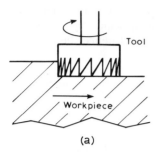

(a)

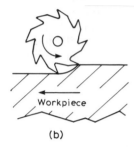

(b)

(c)

Figure 2.42 (a) Face milling. (b) Up milling. (c) Down milling

3 Milling

A milling machine has multiple cutting edges with each edge taking its share of the cutting as the workpiece is fed past them. A wide variety of different forms of tools exist, milling being a very versatile process. *Figure 2.42* illustrates some basic forms of tool and the cutting action. The axis of rotation of the tool can be either horizontal or vertical.

Milling machines can be used, with the appropriate tools, to machine:

(a) Plane surfaces, parallel or at right angles to the base face;
(b) Plane surfaces at an angle relative to the base surface;
(c) Keyways or slots;
(d) Helical flutes and grooves;
(e) Irregular shaped forms;
(f) Circular forms;
(g) Holes;
(h) Thread forms;
(i) Gear teeth.

Milling produces roughness values of the order of 0.8 to 6.5 μm and minimum tolerances of the order of 0.25 mm.

Drilling

Drilling, like milling, involves multiple cutting edges. Because the cutting action takes place within the workpiece the chips have to come out of the hole past the drill which itself largely fills the hole. This can make lubrication and cooling of the tool difficult. Add to this the friction between the body of the drill and the sides of the hole and there is a heat problem which can significantly affect the accuracy with which a hole can be drilled. Drilling gives surface roughnesses of the order of 1.6 to 8.0 μm and minimum tolerances of the order of 0.05 mm.

Drilling machines can also be used for reaming. This is the process whereby a hole is brought to a more exact size by using a multi-edged tool rotating within the hole.

5 Grinding

Grinding is a multi-edge cutting operation employing what could be considered a self-sharpening tool. The grinding wheel has abrasive particles, such as carborundum, bonded in a matrix. As the wheel rotates, these small, hard, brittle, particles cut small chips from the workpiece. As the edges of these particles become blunted, the forces acting on them due to friction increase and eventually the force may become large enough to fracture, or tear, the particle if free from the matrix. The result, either way, is to expose a new cutting surface. Hence the concept of the grinding wheel as being a self sharpening tool.

Because each cutting edge is very small, and the edges are numerous, close dimensional control is possible and very fine surfaces can be produced. Also, because the abrasive particles compose very hard materials, the grinding wheel can be used to machine very hard material workpieces. Grinding is used to:

(a) Remove surplus material from a workpiece;
(b) Improve the dimensional accuracy of the workpiece;
(c) Obtain the required surface finish;
(d) Machine very hard materials which are not so readily turned or milled.

Grinding can give surface roughnesses of the order of 0.1 to 1.6 μm and minimum tolerances of the order of 0.002 mm. Grinding

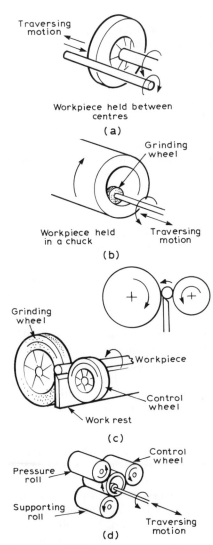

Traversing
motion

Workpiece held between
centres

(a)

Grinding
wheel

Workpiece held
in a chuck

Traversing
motion

(b)

Grinding
wheel

Workpiece

Control
wheel

Work rest

(c)

Control
wheel

Pressure
roll

Supporting
roll

Traversing
motion

(d)

Figure 2.43 (a) Centre-type external cylindrical grinding
(b) Internal cylindrical grinding
(c) Centreless external cylindrical grinding
(d) Centreless internal cylindrical grinding

removes only small amounts of metal at each cut, i.e. very small chips are produced. While this allows manufacture to close tolerances it does however mean that the time taken to produce a unit area of a finished surface is relatively long. The cost is thus high per unit volume of metal removed. For this reason grinding is often used as a finishing process following machining by another method, e.g. milling.

• *Figure 2.43* illustrates some of the basic grinding methods used. Centre-type external grinding is used for producing external cylindrical surfaces where the workpiece can be held between centres and rotated against the grinding wheel. Internal cylindrical grinding, as in *Figure 2.43b*, involves the workpiece being held in a chuck and rotated. With centreless grinding there is no necessity to hold the workpiece between centres or in a chuck. This can reduce total operation time by eliminating the need for centre holes in the workpiece and the time taken to mount the workpiece.

With external centreless grinding two abrasive wheels are used. The larger of these wheels does the actual grinding and rotates at the regular grinding speed. The smaller of the wheels is the control wheel; it rotates at a slower speed and controls the rotation of the workpiece. A work rest is used to keep the workpiece pressing against the face of the control wheel.

With internal centreless grinding, three rolls are used to support the workpiece and impart rotation to it (*Figure 2.43d*).

There are three types of feed operation used with centreless grinding. In through-feed grinding the workpiece has a constant diameter and is fed through the wheels which have been set at a constant separation(*Figure 2.44a*). In order to impart an axial feed to the workpiece the control wheel is tilted slightly, generally less than 7°.

Infeed grinding is used for multidiameter work or any form of work that cannot be passed completely through the wheels. The work rest and the control wheel are retracted and the workpiece placed in position. Then the rotating control wheel advances the workpiece up to the grinding wheel. The control wheel is usually tilted slightly to hold the workpiece against an end stop.

End feed grinding is used with work which is multidiameter but where the length to be ground is too long for the infeed grinding operation. The workpiece is loaded as with infeed grinding but then a feed motion is imparted to the workpiece and it advances through until it meets the end stop. It is thus a mixture of infeed and through feed grinding.

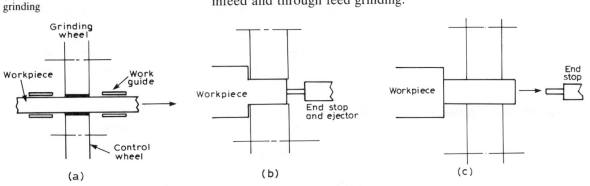

Figure 2.44 (a) Through feed grinding (b) In feed grinding (c) End feed grinding

Finishing processes

After machining, some components undergo a further process in order to produce an improvement in accuracy and an improvement in surface finish. The following methods are used.

1 Grinding

The type of grinding machine used will depend on whether the surface is flat or curved and whether it is an internal or external surface. Thus, for example, a surface grinder may be used for a flat surface and possibly a centreless type grinder for a cylindrical surface. Specially shaped grinders may be used for threads and gears, and other shapes.

The type of finish obtained will depend on the grinding wheel chosen and the operating conditions used. Typically, roughness values of the order of 0.1 to 1.6 μm can be obtained, though with care 0.025 μm is possible.

2 Lapping

Lapping consists of rubbing the surface concerned against a softer material surface with there being a fine abrasive in oil between the two surfaces. The operation can be carried out by a machine. The process is very slow as only small pieces of metal are removed in the process. Typically, roughness values of the order of 0.05 to 0.4 μm can be obtained, though with care 0.0125 μm is possible.

3 Honing

Honing is mainly used for internal cylindrical surfaces. A number of abrasive sticks are mounted on an expanding mandrel (*Figure 2.45*) which is inserted into the hole and adjusted to bear against the walls. As well as rotating, the tool also has a reciprocating motion. A lubricant, such as paraffin, is used. Typically, roughness values of the order of 0.1 to 0.8 μm are produced, though with care 0.025 μm can be produced.

4 Superfinishing

An abrasive block reciprocates across the face of the workpiece, *Figure 2.46* illustrating the type of process involved. A lubricant is used between the surfaces. A controlled amount of pressure is applied to the abrasive block so that when the appropriate amount of surface cutting has taken place, the lubricant film separates the two surfaces and prevents further cutting action. Typically, roughness values of the order of 0.05 to 0.2 μm can be achieved, though with care values as low as 0.0125 μm are possible.

5 Burnishing

Burnishing involves the rubbing of a smooth hard object under considerable pressure over the surface concerned. The high pressure causes the surface protrusions to suffer plastic flow. The term roll burnishing is used when internal or external cylindrical surfaces are burnished using hard rollers.

Because the process involves cold working the resulting surface has better wearing properties. Typically, roughness values of the order of 0.2 to 0.4 μm are obtained, though with care values as low as 0.1 μm are possible.

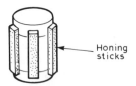

Figure 2.45 Basic format of a honing head

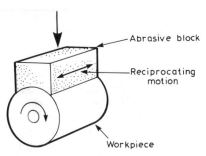

Figure 2.46 Superfinishing

The selection of cutting processes

When selecting a cutting process, the following factors are relevant in determining the optimum process or processes:

1 Operations should be devised so that the minimum amount of material is removed. This reduces materials costs, energy costs involved in the machining and costs due to tool wear.

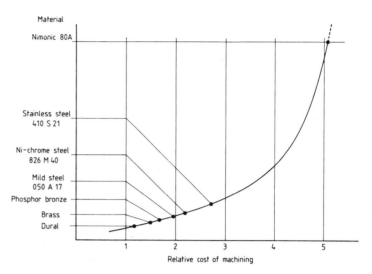

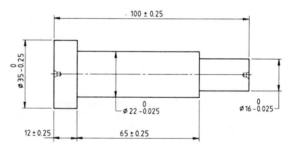

Figure 2.47 Relative cost of machining different materials. (Reproduced with the permission of the British Standards Institution, being taken from 'Manual of British Standards in Engineering Drawing and Design (Hutchinson 1984))

2 The time spent by the labour on the operation should be a minimum to keep labour costs low.

3 The skills required of the labour, again affecting labour costs.

4 The properties of the material being machined should be considered; in particular the hardness.

5 The process, or processes, chosen should take into account the quantity of products involved and the required rate of production.

6 The geometric form of the product should be considered and the process or processes chosen which are the most appropriate.

7 The required surface finish and dimensional accuracy should be considered so that the process or processes chosen can achieve them.

Chapter 1 discussed cutting speeds and the most economical cutting speed. The highest cutting speed is not always the most economical bearing in mind the tool wear involved. *Figure 1.4* illustrates this.

Figure 2.47 illustrates how the relative cost of machining a component is affected by the choice of material for that component. In general, an important factor determining the time taken to cut a material, and hence the cost, is the material hardness; the harder a material the longer it is likely to take to cut. The hardness also however affects the choice of tool material that can be used,

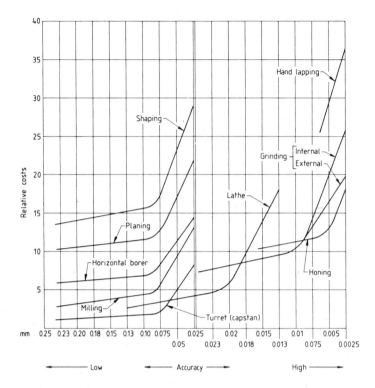

Figure 2.48 Cost of various machine and hand processes for achieving set tolerances. (Reproduced with the permission of the British Standards Institution, being taken from 'Manual of British Standards in Engineering Drawing and Design (Hutchinson 1984))

and also, in the case of very hard materials, the process. Thus, for instance, grinding is a process that can be used with very hard materials, because the tool material, the abrasive particles, can be very hard.

Where a considerable amount of machining occurs, the use of free-machining grades of materials should always be considered in order to keep costs down by keeping the cutting time to as low a value as possible.

Machining operations vary quite significantly in cost, particularly if the operation is considered in terms of the cost necessary for a particular machine to achieve particular tolerances. *Figure 2.48* shows how the relative costs vary for achieving set tolerances. Thus to achieve a tolerance of 0.10 mm, the rank order of the processes is:

Shaping	most expensive
Planing	
Horizontal borer	
Milling	
Turret (capstan)	least expensive

The cost of all the processes increases as the required tolerance is increased. At high tolerances grinding is one of the cheapest processes. The different machining operations also produce different surface finishes, the following table indicating the approximate rank order:

Planing and shaping	R_a	15 μm to 0.8 μm	Least smooth
Drilling	R_a	8 μm to 1.6 μm	
Milling	R_a	6.3 μm to 0.8 μm	
Turning	R_a	6.3 μm to 0.4 μm	
Grinding	R_a	1.6 μm to 0.1 μm	Most smooth

The choice of process will depend on the geometric form of the product being produced. For plane surfaces the processes are shaping, planing, face milling and surface grinding. For machining externally cylindrical surfaces, there are turning and grinding. For internal cylindrical surfaces, processes are drilling, boring and grinding. For flat and contoured surfaces and slots, there are milling and grinding.

Machining, in general, is a relatively expensive process when compared with many other methods of forming materials. The machining process is, however, a very flexible process which allows of the generation of a wide variety of forms. A significant part of the total machining cost of a product is due to setting-up times when there is a change from one machining step to another. By reducing the number of machining steps and hence the number of setting-up times, a significant saving becomes possible. Thus the careful sequencing of machining operations and the careful choice of machine to be used is important.

Forming and generating using machine tools

In general the profile of a component can be produced by a cutting process involving forming or generating. With forming, a specially shaped tool is used which has the required profile on its cutting edge. Thus, for example, in the process known as gear forming, the cutter used has the profile of the tooth space on the gearwheel being produced. The shape of the workpiece left after the cutting operation is the reverse image of the tool shape.

With generating, the tool shape has no effect on the workpiece shape produced by the cutting process, this shape being determined by the way the tool is constrained to move during the cutting operation.

In many machining processes there is a mixture of forming and generating for the production of the required workpiece profile. For instance, when cutting the screw thread on a workpiece using a single-point tool on a centre lathe, the tool has the required shape for the thread profile and so the thread profile is formed however the helix of the screw is generated.

Screw thread production

There are seven main methods by which screw threads can be produced. Two of these, however, are not suitable for mass production but are used extensively in small batch or unit production. These methods are taps and dies, and single-point turning using a lathe. The following are the main characteristics of the various methods.

1 Taps and dies
Taps are used for the cutting of an internal thread by hand. The tap is a fluted screw of hardened steel and is screwed into a plain

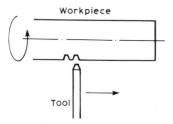

Figure 2.49 Single point turning

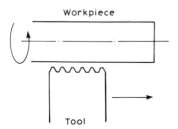

Figure 2.50 Chasing

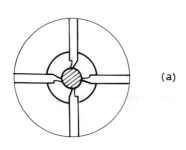

(a)

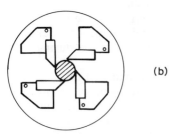

(b)

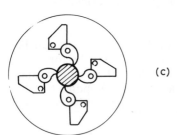

(c)

Figure 2.51 Types of die head. (a) Radial die.
(b) Tangential die. (c) Circular die

hole in order to cut the thread on the wall of the hole. Dies are used for cutting an external thread by hand. They are essentially a nut which is screwed onto the plain shaft concerned in order to cut the thread on its surface. Both these manual methods are slow.

2 Single-point turning using a lathe
A specially shaped tool, having the required thread profile, is moved along the length of the rod being given a thread while the rod is rotated (*Figure 2.49*). Both external and internal threads can be cut. The process is slow and requires a skilled operator.

3 Chasing
Thread chasing is similar in cutting method to single-point turning using a lathe but instead of a single-point cutter a multi-point cutter is used (*Figure 2.50*). The chaser tool is moved while the workpiece rotates along it during the thread cutting. Both external and internal threads can be cut. Chasing is employed mainly for large diameter threads. A capstan lathe or turret lathe is used and the operation can be carried out quickly.

4 Self-opening die heads
Self-opening die heads can be used with capstan and turret lathes for external thread cutting. The solid die used for manual cutting of threads has the disadvantage that it has to be unscrewed from the workpiece to remove it, thus limiting it to manual production. Self-opening dies can be made to open automatically when the required length of thread has been produced.

There are three types of self-opening die head, all have four sets of adjustable multiple point cutters but the way in which they are arranged differs. *Figure 2.51* shows the three types. With the radial die, the cutters are positioned radially; on the tangential die the cutters are arranged tangentially and on the circular die the cutters are circular. The radial type of die is the one most used.

Collapsing taps are similar to self-opening die heads. Radial and circular cutter forms exist, the radial type being used for smaller thread sizes and the circular for the larger sizes. Such taps are used for internal threads.

5 Thread rolling
This method is used for a high percentage of external threads that are mass produced. It is a cold-forming operation in which a blank is rolled between dies in order to form the threads. The rolling applies compressive forces to the material of the blank and these forces are sufficiently high to cause the material to flow into the die and form the upper portion of the thread (*Figure 2.52*). Because of this flow, the blank has only to be the mean diameter of the thread.

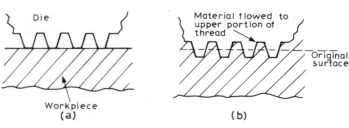

Figure 2.52 Thread rolling. (a) Initially, (b) after rolling

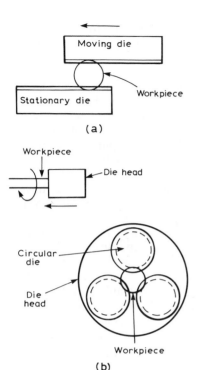

(a)

(b)

Figure 2.53 (a) Flat die rolling.
(b) Circular die rolling

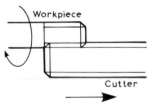

Figure 2.54 Thread milling

There are two basic methods of thread rolling, one employing flat dies and the other circular dies (*Figure 2.53*). Flat die rolling is a very fast process and is used in a fully-automatic production machine. Circular die rolling is not as fast but can also be used as an automatic production process.

Because thread rolling is a cold-working process the surface hardness, strength and fatigue resistance of the material are improved. However the materials used must be reasonably ductile and not have too great a hardness. The way the threads are formed gives a grain flow which follows the contours of the threads and so is beneficial. The surface finish is also good, a roughness of about 0.2 μm.

6 *Thread milling*

This method is used for work of large diameter, generally too large for die heads. With the workpiece initially stationary the cutter cuts inwards to the full-thread depth. Then the workpiece is rotated slowly while the rotating cutter is simultaneously moved longitudinally (*Figure 2.54*). One revolution of the workpiece is all that is necessary to complete the thread.

7 *Thread grinding*

This method can produce very accurate external threads; it can also be used on hardened materials. A grinding wheel is used which has annular thread grooves formed around its periphery. There are two methods, transverse grinding and plunge cut grinding (*Figure 2.55*).

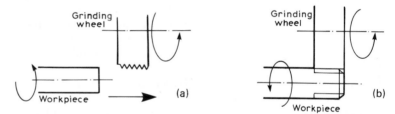

Figure 2.55 (a) Traverse grinding. (b) Plunge cut grinding

In traverse grinding the wheel is first set to full thread depth, then the rotating workpiece is fed past the wheel. In plunge thread grinding the workpiece is initially stationary and the grinding wheel, while rotating, is plunged to full thread depth. The workpiece is rotated while simultaneously moving longitudinally. Just one revolution of the workpiece occurs, the method being similar to the thread milling described above.

When selecting the thread production process, the following points should be considered. If mass production is required then taps and dies and single-point turning using a lathe are too slow. Thread rolling is a high-rate production method and can produce threads with greater strength and higher fatigue resistance than other methods because it is a cold working process. This method is generally restricted to fine pitch threads and relatively small diameters because of the high pressures needed for the cold working. Self-opening die heads with capstan or turret lathes, or automatic machines, is used for general external thread cutting. Thread chasing is used for general thread cutting where the workpiece is too large a diameter for self-opening die heads.

Thread milling is used for large, generally special form, threads. Thread grinding is a versatile, highly accurate, method of cutting threads.

Gear cutting

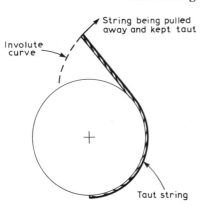

Figure 2.56 The involute curve

In order to minimize friction and wear, gears are designed to have a rolling motion between mating teeth rather than a sliding motion. The most commonly used tooth shape that allows this type of motion is based on an involute curve. If a piece of string is wrapped round a cylinder (*Figure 2.56*) and then pulled away from the cylinder, the line described by the end of the string is an involute curve.

The cheapest of all gear types are the spur gears. These have straight teeth and are used to connect parallel shafts (*Figure 2.57*). With helical gears, the teeth lie along a helix. These gears can connect either parallel or non-parallel shafts. They are stronger and quieter than spur gears, but are more expensive to produce.

There are a number of methods by which gears can be manufactured. Mass production tends to be by machining and by cold rolling but powder metallurgy, extrusion and blanking can also be used. For gears having high accuracy, machining is primarily used. The three main methods used for machining gears are planing, shaping and hobbing. These processes are generating processes rather than forming processes.

1 Form cutting

This process involves using a tool having the same form as the space between the adjacent teeth in the gearwheel to be produced. *Figure 2.58* shows the basic principle. A milling machine can be used with just a single-point cutter to cut each tooth separately. Such a process is slow but is a simple and flexible method. It is likely to be used only where a small number of gears have to be machined.

2 Planing

Figure 2.59 shows the basic principle of the planing process. With the blank stationary initially, the cutter is fed in to a full tooth depth with the cutter reciprocating. The blank then rotates and the cutter feeds longitudinally as indicated in the diagram. The involute shape is then generated. After a few teeth have been cut the cutter is withdrawn and moved back to its starting position and the cycle repeated. This process is used for the production of external spur gears and helical gears.

3 Shaping

Figure 2.60 shows the basic principle of gear shaping. The cutter is first fed into the full depth with the cutter reciprocating and the blank stationary. Then the cutter and blank both rotate and

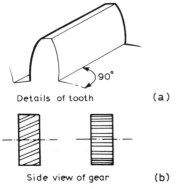

Figure 2.57 (a) Spur gear. (b) Helical gear

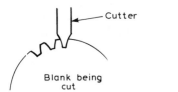

Figure 2.58 Form cutting of gears

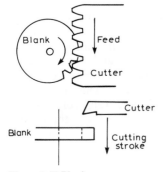

Figure 2.59 Planing

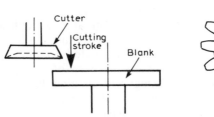

Figure 2.60 Shaping

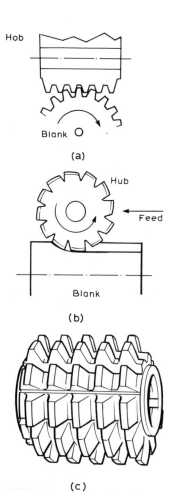

Figure 2.61 (a) The hobbing process. (b) The hob

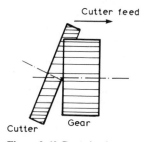

Figure 2.62 Gear shaving

continue rotating until all the teeth have been cut. For mass production there may be more than one cutter so that more than one gear can be produced at the same time. The process is used for the production of spur gears, helical gears and other more complicated gear patterns, both external and internal.

Shaping is a versatile process and is faster than planing although it is not completely continuous due to the reciprocating cutting action. The planing operation also has this reciprocating cutting action but only a few teeth are cut at any one operation before the cutter has to be reset.

4 Hobbing

This is the fastest process as it is completely continuous. The cutting tool, the gear hob, consists of a row of cutting teeth wrapped round a cylinder in a helix (*Figure 2.61*). With both the hob and the blank rotating, the hob is fed into the blank to the full depth and then the hob fed across the blank face. The process is a milling operation. It can be used for both external spur gears and helical gears. Accurate gears can be produced at a very high speed.

5 Cold rolling

Cold rolling is used for the production of many gears, the process essentially being the same as that used for the production of threads on workpieces by rolling. Because the process is a cold forming operation the surface hardness, strength and fatigue resistance of the material are improved by the process.

6 Moulding

Gears made of plastics instead of metal are finding an increasing amount of use in conditions where only light loads are experienced and where high accuracy is not required. Plastic gears can be made by moulding (see Chapter 3).

After gears have been cut from the blank, a gear finishing stage is often required in order to obtain accurate tooth profiles and smooth faces to the teeth. The most common finishing process is gear shaving. The shaving cutter is in the form of a gear having sharp cutting edges on each tooth. The shaving cutter and the gear are run in mesh and the small amounts of material removed necessary to bring the gear to the required accuracy (*Figure 2.62*). Following shaving the gear might be hardened before being subject to lapping. In this process the gear is run in contact with cast-iron lapping gears under a flow of very fine abrasive in oil.

Grinding is an alternative to gear shaving and lapping generally following hardening. The grinding operation may be a forming or a generating operation and the result is a highly accurate gear. The gear shaving and lapping processes do not produce gears so accurately or of such good quality, but they are cheaper than grinding.

2.6 METAL REMOVAL

The machining methods previously considered have all involved removing metal from the workpiece by cutting involving a tool, the tool being harder than the material of the workpiece. There are however other methods of removing metal which do not involve cutting using a tool. These methods can be summarized as electrochemical machining, electrical discharge machining and chemical machining. All these methods have the great advantage over traditional machining in that the hardness of the material of the workpiece is of no consequence, this property not affecting the rate of metal removal.

1 Electrochemical machining (ECM)

Electrochemical machining involves an electric current being passed between two electrodes dipping into an electrolyte. The workpiece is used as the positive electrode, known as the anode (the electrode connected to the positive side of the d.c. supply) and the tool is the negative electrode, known as the cathode. The tool is not in contact with the workpiece and carries out no cutting action. The tool is merely a piece of suitable conducting metal that is shaped as the reverse image of the form required of the workpiece. Thus if a hollow is required in the workpiece the tool has a hill. The workpiece and the tool are positioned very close together, with generally less than 1 mm between them. The space between the workpiece and the tool is filled with electrolyte which is constantly being replenished. *Figure 2.63* illustrates the arrangement.

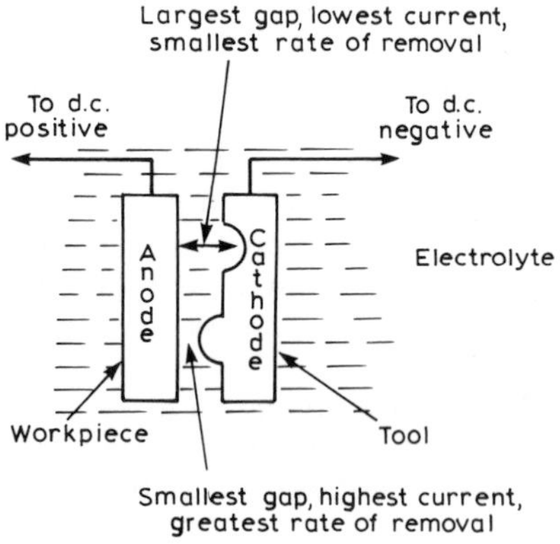

When a d.c. supply is connected to the two electrodes a current passes between them. Very high currents are used. The term current density is used to describe the current in relation to the surface area of the electrode concerned. Thus current densities of the order of 50 to 1900 A/cm^2 are used. The result of this is that metal is removed from the workpiece and goes into solution. The metal is removed at the greatest rate from that part of the workpiece which is closest to the tool. Thus where there is a hill on the tool surface, the gap between it and the workpiece is smallest and it is here that there is the greatest rate of metal removal from the workpiece. Where there is a valley on the tool, the gap between it and the workpiece is greatest and the rate of removal of metal the least. The effect of this is that the workpiece has metal removed at different rates from the different parts of it and a reverse image of the profile of the tool is produced.

During the metal removal the tool is advanced towards the workpiece at a rate which maintains a constant separation between the two; the electrolyte being pumped between the two surfaces at a speed of generally about 10 to 50 m/s. This speed is necessary in order to sweep away the waste products that are produced and allow the current density and so metal removal to be maintained. Metal removal rates of the order of 10 to 300 mm^3 per second are possible, this rate being independent of the hardness of the material, being only determined by the rate at which metal atoms in the workpiece go into solution. This is essentially a function of the current.

Electrochemical machining has the following advantages when compared with traditional machining:

(a) The tool does not wear (provided a suitable material is used which is not corroded by the electrolyte);
(b) There are no thermal or mechanical stresses on the workpiece during the metal removal;
(c) By using shaped electrodes on either side of the workpiece three dimensional machining can occur.

During electrochemical machining, metal removal occurs not only from that part of the workpiece directly opposite the tool but

Largest gap, lowest current, smallest rate of removal

To d.c. positive

To d.c. negative

Anode

Cathode

Electrolyte

Workpiece

Tool

Smallest gap, highest current, greatest rate of removal

Figure 2.63 Electrochemical machining

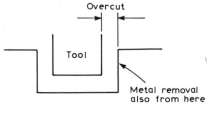

Figure 2.64 Overcutting

also from those parts of the workpiece round the side of the tool (*Figure 2.64*). The result of this is an overcutting, e.g. in the production of a hole in the workpiece the hole will have a greater diameter than the diameter of the tool. Typically the overcut is of the order of 0.02 to 0.1 mm.

The surface roughness produced is of the order of 0.2 to 0.4 µm, a fine surface, and tolerances of the order of 0.05 mm achieved.

The disadvantages of electrochemical machining are:

(a) The basic cost of the equipment is fairly high;
(b) The tool has to be made of non-corrosive material and has to be rigidly mounted, as also has the workpiece, bearing in mind the high rate of flow of electrolyte between tool and workpiece.

Electrochemical machining can produce small deep holes, odd-shaped holes and cavities, three dimensional shapes, and can deal with high strength high hardness materials. The process finds application in the machining of high temperature alloy forgings to the required finish and tolerances, jet engine blade aerofoils, turbine wheels with integral blades.

2 Electrical discharge machining (ECM)

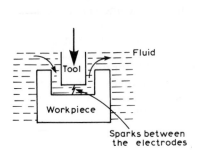

Figure 2.65 Electrical discharge machining

In electrical discharge machining (ECM) material is removed by the action of electrical discharges—sparks—on the surface of the workpiece. The tool and the workpiece are submerged in a fluid, such as paraffin or light oil. This fluid normally acts as an insulator. A voltage is then applied between the workpiece and the tool and increased until the insulating properties of the fluid break down and a massive pulse of current flows between the tool and the workpiece. This causes part of the workpiece to be vapourised and hence metal to be removed, as the vapourised atoms of metal are swept away by the flow of the fluid.

The fluid is continuously pumped through the assembly with a filter being used in the pumping line to extract the metal that has been removed from the workpiece and the sludge of black particles, mainly carbon, that is produced from the breakdown of the fluid. *Figure 2.65* illustrates the basic principle of electrical discharge machining.

The electrical discharges between the tool and the workpiece occur where the distance between the tool and the workpiece is a minimum. The tool is thus a reverse image of the shape required from the workpiece. During the machining by this method the tool is moved so that the distance between the tool and workpiece remains constant, generally about 0.02 mm.

It is not only the workpiece that has metal removed during the discharge, the tool also looses material. The rate of loss of material from the tool can be minimised by suitable choice of the material for the tool and the choice of operating conditions. A high melting point for the tool material is one of the conditions for low tool wear, for this reason graphite (melting point 3500°C) is widely used.

The metal removal rate with electrical discharge machining is fairly low, i.e. of the order of 1 mm^3 per second. Tolerances of the order of 0.05 mm can be achieved with surface roughness values of the order of 1.6 to 3.2 µm. As with electrochemical machining metal removal occurs from the workpiece not only directly underneath the tool but also round the sides of the tool. This overcut (see *Figure 2.61*) is typically about 0.005 to 0.2 mm.

The advantages of electric discharge machining when compared with traditional machining are:

(a) The hardness of the material being machined is not a factor, as long as the material can conduct a current it can be machined;
(b) any shape that can be produced for the tool can be reproduced, thus very complicated machining can occur;
(c) there are no mechanical stresses in the workpiece during the metal removal.

The disadvantages of electric discharge machining are:

(a) Tool wear occurs and in, for example, the production of deep holes the tool is likely to need redressing;
(b) After cutting, the workpiece will have a surface layer different from the parent metal. Typically there are three parts to the layer—an inner annealed layer of hardness less than that of the parent material; a layer which has reached melting point but has not been removed and which remains as a recast layer; an upper layer formed by molten particles being redeposited on the surface. In steel workpieces this layer may be much harder and more brittle than the parent material and can reduce the fatigue endurance limits. Some finishing process may thus be used, after electric discharge machining, in order to remove the layer;
(c) The process is relatively slow.

An important modification of the electric discharge machining principle is the continuous wire electrode machine (*Figure 2.66*). Instead of using a shaped tool as one electrode a wire is used. This wire, is approx. 0.25 mm dia but can be smaller. It is continuously fed into the machining situation, at a velocity of about 0.1 to 8 m per minute. Enough wire is generally available for the operation to continue for twenty-four hours or more. Complex shapes can be cut in materials up to about 15 cm thick, at rates of the order of 0.5 mm per minute. The process is used with NC and CNC.

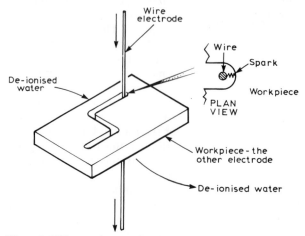

Figure 2.66 The continuous wire electrode electric discharge machine

3 Chemical machining

In chemical machining the material is removed from the workpiece by exposing it to a chemical reagent. The terms chemical milling, photofabrication and chemical blanking sometimes are also used to describe the process. The metal removal is fairly simple, the component being either immersed in or exposed to a spray of chemical reagent. The type of chemical reagent used depends on the metal concerned. The component remains exposed to the reagent until the required amount of metal has been removed. The more complex part of the operation is however the method by which parts of the component are masked so that metal removal only takes place in certain areas.

A common masking method involves the use of photosensitive resists. The workpiece is coated with a light-sensitive emulsion. When this has dried a photographic negative, of the master pattern that is required, is placed against the workpiece and light passed through it and onto the sensitive emulsion on the workpiece. When the workpiece is immersed in a developing agent, those areas that were not exposed to the light are removed leaving a mask over the exposed parts of the workpiece. When the chemical reagent is then used, those areas that are not masked have metal removed, the other areas because of their masking are not affected.

This method is used in the production of electronic circuit boards and other components which are often very complex, small and rather thin, and would present problems if tackled in any other way.

Chemical machining can be applied to almost any metal and can be used with both small and large surface areas. The process does not produce any mechanical or thermal stresses in the material, but it may release existing residual stresses already in the material and so some warping may occur. Surfaces typically have a roughness of 1.6 to 6.3 µm and tolerances of the order of 0.075 mm can be achieved.

The disadvantages of chemical machining are that the rate of metal removal is fairly slow per unit area exposed. If the metal of the workpiece is not homogeneous different removal rates can occur for different parts of the workpiece. Another problem is that the chemical reagent acts on all exposed surfaces. Consequently as the depth of metal removal into the workpiece increases there will be an increasing tendency to undercut and remove metal from under the masked surface (*Figure 2.67*).

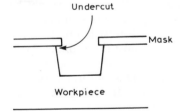

Figure 2.67 Undercutting with chemical machining

2.7 SURFACE FINISHES

A large proportion of products are given a form of decorative or protective surface treatment to complete their manufacturing process. In some cases there may be a need for only cleaning the surface, but this is also likely to be necessary before applying any other form of finish. Cleaning can be accomplished by mechanical, chemical or ultrasonic means.

Mechanical cleaning can involve various methods of abrasive cleaning in which an abrasive agent, such as sand or shot, is directed against the surface to be cleaned. Another mechanical method involves high speed rotatory wire brushes being applied to the surface. A further form of mechanical cleaning involves placing the parts to be cleaned in a drum, along with some abrasive material such as sand of special abrasive pellets. The drum is then either rotated, to give a tumbling action, or vibrated back-and-forth.

Chemical cleaning is commonly used at some stage in the production process to remove dirt, scale, oil, grease, etc. Various forms of chemical cleaning are used. Alkaline cleaning uses such materials as caustic soda and is widely employed. Solvents are often used when oils and greases are involved and for metals such as aluminium or zinc which would be attacked by alkaline cleaners.

Ultrasonic cleaning is used where fairly small parts have to be made very clean. The parts are placed in a cleaning bath of liquid and very high frequency sound, ultrasonic sound, is passed through the liquid, which causes the liquid to cavitate. This term is used to describe the process in which the sound causes small vacuum pockets to be produced in the liquid. These pockets almost immediately collapse and the resulting action causes a scrubbing action.

Following cleaning, a decorative or protective surface treatment can be applied to the surfaces of a product. Such finishes can be either an additive coating of the surface or a conversion of the surface layers of the product. Common examples of additive coatings are paints and electroplating; an example of conversion layers is anodising.

Painting may be carried out using dipping, hand or automatic spraying and electrocoating. With dipping the parts are dipped into the paint, either manually or as part of an automated process. This method is used where the entire component needs the same coat of paint, often with small components where spraying could result in a considerable loss of paint due to overspraying and for the priming coat of paint which precedes the finishing coats. The disadvantages of this method are that very thin layers cannot be produced and there is a tendency for the paint to run and produce a wavy surface and a drip of paint at the lowest point. In spray painting paint is atomised and directed against the product. With conventional spraying there can be a very significant wastage of paint and also there is difficulty in obtaining a uniform coverage. Electrostatic spraying gives better results. In this process the atomised paint is given an electrostatic charge. These charged particles are then attracted to the workpiece, which is generally electrically earthed. Under reasonable conditions, more than 90% of the paint can be deposited on the product by this method.

Electroplating involves making the workpiece the negative electrode, i.e. the cathode, in a suitable electrolyte while the metal to be deposited is the positive electrode, i.e. the anode (*Figure 2.68*). Tin, cadmium, chromium, copper, gold, silver and zinc are examples of metals that are used to electroplate products. In some cases more than one material may be used to coat the workpiece, nickel often being used as an undercoating to gold or silver.

Anodising is a conversion process used with aluminium. Unlike electroplating, the workpiece is the anode in an electrolyte and instead of a layer of material being added to the surface the result is the conversion of the surface layers to aluminium oxide. Unlike the addition processes, anodising does not cause an increase in size of the product.

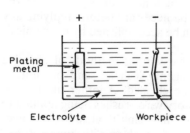

Figure 2.68 Electroplating

This short section has barely touched the subject of finishes, particularly those used to reduce corrosion. Further information can be found in *Materials Technology 4*, by W. Bolton (Butterworths 1981) or in greater detail in *Metal Corrosion* by T.K. Ross, an Engineering Design Guide, No. 21, published for the Design Council, the British Standards Institution and the Council of Engineering Institutions by Oxford University Press (1977).

QUESTIONS

(1) Compare sand casting and die casting as methods for the production of a product.

(2) Why is die casting not suitable for the production of small quantities of components?

(3) Under what conditions would investment casting be more economic than die casting?

(4) Suggest a casting process for the following situation. A small one-off casting is required using aluminium, there is a lot of fine detail which has to be reproduced and a good surface finish is required.

(5) State two design features that have to be taken into account when designing a product to be produced by casting.

(6) Under what circumstances is casting likely to be the optimum process?

(7) What are the benefits and disadvantages of using hot working as opposed to cold working?

(8) Compare the surface finishes produced by hot and cold rolling.

(9) How are hollow shapes produced by extrusion?

(10) It is proposed to use extrusion for the production of seamless aluminium tubing. What is approximately the largest diameter tubing that could be produced? About what size would be the maximum length possible?

(11) Compare forging and casting as methods of production for a product.

(12) What types of product is the upsetting process used for?

(13) Suggest a process for the production of the section used for aluminium window frames.

(14) Explain the basic process of shearing that occurs when a punch is used to shear a metal sheet.

(15) Explain how piercing and blanking operations can be used for the production of washers.

(16) Explain the need for bending allowances in the production of components by bending.

(17) How does the cross-section of a bar change when it is bent?

(18) Give two examples of products that could be produced using bending.

(19) What type of materials have to be used with deep drawing?

(20) Describe the process of deep drawing.

(21) How is the wrinkling of the material during deep drawing prevented?

(22) At what position in a deep drawn product is failure likely to occur during the drawing process?

(23) What is ironing?

(24) Compare rigid die and flexible die methods of drawing and state the situations under which flexible dies would be more economic.

(25) Give an example of products that can be produced using deep drawing.

(26) When a sheet of material is bent, the side that is in compression may buckle or distort. How can this be prevented?

(27) How does flow turning differ from spinning?

(28) What type of materials can be used with impact extrusion?

(29) What is high velocity metal forming and what types of product are produced by this process?

(30) Suggest processes that might be used for the following products:
(a) a toothpaste tube from a very soft alloy; (b) the reflector concave dish for a satellite TV receiving aerial, using aluminium or mild steel; (c) rivets; (d) an aluminium can for a drink or food storage; (e) the formed wing of a car; (f) a hollow hexagonal length of brass rod; (g) a spanner; (h) railway lines; (i) a kitchen pan.

(31) Calculate the maximum punch force needed to blank a circle of radius 20 mm from a steel sheet of thickness 1.5 mm and having a shear strength of 420 MPa.

(32) Calculate the maximum punch force needed for a single stage piercing and blanking operation in which a washer with an external radius of 20 mm and an internal radius of 12 mm is produced from material of thickness 1.5 mm and having a shear strength of 430 MPa.

(33) Estimate the work done in blanking a square of side 80 mm from sheet of thickness 2.0 mm if the penetration is 25% and the material has a shear strength of 430 MPa.

(34) Why in a blanking or piercing operation with a press might the punch or the die have shear on it? Explain what shear is.

(35) What force will need to be applied by the punch in a bending operation with a press if a right angle bend is to be produced in mild steel sheet of thickness 3.0 mm and width 100 mm if the material has a yield stress of 200 MPa.

(36) What is the force necessary to draw a cup 30 mm dia. from a blank of 60 mm dia. and sheet of thickness 2.0 mm if the material has a yield stress of 200 MPa?

(37) How do combination press tools differ from progression press tools?

(38) Outline the processes used to produce a sintered product.

(39) What are the advantages and the limitations of powder techniques for producing products?

(40) What makes some materials easy to machine and others difficult?

(41) Explain why free cutting steels have good machineability.

(42) Rank the cutting operations of turning, planing, milling, drilling and grinding in the order of surface finish, rough to fine.

(43) Why are turret and capstan lathes preferred to centre lathes for mass production work?

(44) List five types of form that milling machines, with appropriate tools, can be used to produce in a workpiece.

(45) State three types of work that can be carried out by grinding.

(46) How does centreless grinding differ from centre-type grinding?

(47) What are the three types of feed operation used with centreless grinding?

(48) Which type of feed operation would be used with centreless grinding if the workpiece was a long shaft of constant cross-section that had to be uniformly brought to the required tolerance.

(49) Rank the finishing operations of grinding, lapping, honing, superfinishing and burnishing in order of the surface finish produced, rough to fine.

(50) State five factors that have to be considered in determining which cutting process to use for a particular operation.

(51) Rank the cutting operations of turning using a capstan lathe, milling, planing and shaping in the order of least expensive to most costly to produce work to a set tolerance (say 0.05 mm).

(52) Distinguish between the terms forming and generating when applied to cutting processes.

(53) Select a screw thread production process that could be used for (a) fine pitch external threads on a small diameter at a high production rate, (b) external threads on a large diameter for mass production.

(54) Rank the gear cutting methods of planing, shaping and hobbing in order of speed of production.

(55) Stage the stages generally occurring in a gear finishing operation.

(56) State the advantages and disadvantages of electrochemical machining when compared with traditional machining.

(57) State a typical type of product that could be produced by electrochemical machining.

(58) State the advantages and disadvantages of electric discharge machining when compared with traditional machining.

(59) Explain the operation of the continuous wire electrode machine version of electric discharge machining and state the type of operation for which it is used.

(60) State the type of product that is produced by chemical machining.

(61) What is the difference between an addition type and a conversion type of finish that will affect the design of a component?

(62) State the type of sequence that is likely to be adopted in applying a finish, such as paint, to a product.

(63) State three different types of cleaning that can be used with metals.

(64) State three reasons why a finish may be applied to the surfaces of a product.

3 Forming processes–polymers

After working through this chapter you should be able to:

Appraise the type of product that may be produced by (a) casting processes; (b) moulding processes; (c) extrusion processes, (d) calendering; (e) forming and (f) machining; understanding the basic principles of the various processes.
Recognise the limitations and merits of the various processes.
Justify the selection of a particular process as viable in relation to quality, quantity and cost.

3.1 POLYMER MATERIALS

Polymers can be divided into two groups—thermoplastics and thermosetting. Thermoplastic materials can be softened and re-softened indefinitely by the application of heat, provided the temperature is not so high as to cause decomposition. Such materials can be formed into different shapes by the application of heat. Examples of such materials are polyethylene (polythene), polyvinyl chloride (p.v.c.), polyamide (Nylon), polycarbonate and cellulose acetate.

Thermosetting materials undergo a chemical change when they are subject to heat; this change cannot be changed by the application of further heating. Typical thermosetting materials are phenol formaldehyde (Bakelite), urea formaldehyde and melamine formaldehyde.

Polymers are produced by a process called polymerization, a process in which many small molecules combine to form a more complex large molecule. Such a molecule has a chain-like structure with hundreds or thousands of identical groups of atoms all linked together. With thermoplastics, the process often stops at the polymerization stage and the resulting material then has a large number of these long molecular chains. With thermosetting materials the process does not stop at that point but continues with cross links being established between different chains and the establishment of a three dimensional network of interlocked molecules.

Both thermoplastic and thermosetting polymers have relatively low densities, relatively low strength and stiffness, low electrical conductivity, low thermal conductivity, low specific heat capacity, high coefficient of thermal expansion and are softened or degraded at temperatures not far removed from the boiling point of water.

For most purposes other materials are added to the polymer to make the material for processing into products, the term plastic generally being used for this 'mixed' material. The additives may be in the form of solids, liquids or gases. The purpose of the additives can be either to improve the properties, reduce the cost, improve the mouldability, or add colour. In many instances the plastic may consist of more than half its weight, or volume, as additive.

The following are some typical examples of additives. Glass fibres can be added to improve the strength of the material, and to make it less ductile but stiffer. Mica may be added to improve the electrical resistance. Liquids may be added to improve the flow characteristics of the material during processing, the liquid acting like a lubricant between the polymer chains. One form of additive is a gas, the result being foamed or expanded materials.

The flow behaviour of polymers A material can be considered to be elastic when the deformation produced in the material is wholly recovered after the removal of the force causing the deformation. For example, this is the type of behaviour that we might expect of a metal in the solid state. However if we consider liquids, deformation means flow. The term used to describe the flow properties is viscosity. It can be considered to be the resistance of a fluid during flow. The higher the viscosity the more resistance there is to flow. A fluid is said to be Newtonian when its viscosity is independent of shear stress and time. Water, for example, is a Newtonian fluid while many paints are non-Newtonian in that if you press the brush harder against the paint its viscosity decreases and it flows more easily. This enables the paint to be spread over a surface. When however the brush pressure is removed the viscosity increases and the paint thus does not flow so readily and hence does not drip.

Polymers exhibit both elastic and viscous responses to applied forces and are therefore described as being visco-elastic. Thus when a force is applied they can show:

1 An instantaneous elastic deformation.
2 A delayed and recoverable elastic deformation, in other words the material continues to become deformed some time after the force has been applied. They show a creep which is recoverable.
3 An irrecoverable deformation due to the flow of polymer chains past each other.

The above behaviour of polymers, in the solid state, has to be taken into account in the use made of the material. This behaviour also has implications for the processing methods used to form products. Polymers also are non-Newtonian in their flow behaviour, the viscosity decreasing in much the same way as the paint. The following are some of the ways the above behaviour affects processing methods:

1 Injection moulding can employ a screw or a ram to compress the polymer and force it out into a mould. A screw, however, applies higher shear rates to the polymer than a ram and so the polymer flows more easily.
2 An alternative to applying shear to a polymer to reduce its viscosity is to heat it—the higher the temperature the lower the viscosity. However in using a thermoplastic in, say, injection moulding the mould has to be cooled in order to cool the thermoplastic component and enable it to be removed from the mould. The higher the temperature at which the polymer is introduced into the mould the longer the time that will need to

occur before it is cold enough to remove. Shearing thus has an advantage over heating in that the time taken to obtain the product is less.

3 When extruded material emerges from the die a phenomena called die swell occurs. This, as the name implies, is a swelling of the material so that it is not the same size as it was when in the die. This can be considered to be due to the delayed and recoverable elastic deformation mentioned earlier. Because the swelling is not necessarily the same in all directions the shape of the extruded component can change.

3.2   FORMING PROCESSES

The processes used with polymers can be considered to be divided into two groups—primary processes and secondary processes. Primary processes involve the fabrication of the component in a single operation from the polymer. Casting, moulding, extrusion and calendering are examples of such processes. With secondary processes a product of a primary process, e.g. a sheet of polymer, is transformed into a finished product. Forming and machining are examples of such processes.

1 Casting

A number of casting methods are employed, but for polymers casting is not like the casting of metals where the hot liquid metal is poured into the mould. Few polymers can be heated to a high enough temperature to flow well enough to be used in such an operation.

One form of casting involves mixing, in a mould, substances of relatively short molecular chains, with any required additives, so that polymerisation, i.e. the production of long-chain molecules, occurs during the chemical reaction which leads to the solid product being produced. For such polymers the term 'cold-setting' is used. This process is used for encapsulating small electrical components, producing tubes, rods and sheets. It can be used with both thermoplastics and thermosets.

Powder casting involves the melting of a powdered polymer inside a heated mould which may be either stationary or rotated during the operation. The term rotational moulding is often used to describe the process when the mould is rotated. The effect of the rotation is to cause the polymer to coat the inside walls of the mould and so produce a hollow article. Holes are not possible though inserts can be used. The process is used with thermoplastics for producing containers, e.g. large milk storage tanks, canisters and crates. Powder casting can also be used to coat surfaces with films of polymers, e.g. non-stick surfaces of cooking pans.

Slush casting involves a fine polymer powder suspended in a liquid (this being the slush) being coated onto the inside of a heated mould. The liquid evaporates and the polymer particles fuse together to form a thin layer of solid polymer. This method is used to produce hollow articles which have fine details, e.g. some plastic toys and plastic gloves.

2 Moulding

A widely used process for thermoplastics, and to some extent for thermosetting materials, is injection moulding. In this process the polymer is fed into the cold end of the injection cylinder

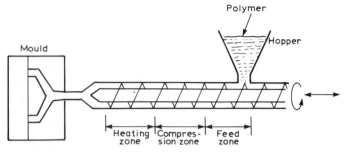

Figure 3.1 Injection moulding

(*Figure 3.1*). A rotating screw, or a ram, then compresses the material and passes it through a heated section and then injects the polymer into the mould. In the case of thermoplastic materials the mould has water cooling. When the material has sufficiently cooled the component is ejected.

With a thermosetting material the same procedure is adopted but the mould is heated and the component can be ejected without waiting for the component to cool, though the material must be held in the mould for a sufficient time for the curing to be completed. The production rate possible with thermoplastics is faster than that possible with thermosetting materials.

Complex shapes with inserts, holes, threads, etc can be produced but enclosed hollow shapes are not possible. Typical products are beer or milk bottle crates, toys, control knobs for electronic equipment, tool handles and pipe fittings. The size of the products can vary from the control knob size, a mass of perhaps 15 g, up to pallets perhaps 1.0 m square and having a mass of many kilogrammes.

The cost of the moulds used with injection moulding is high and thus it is only with large production runs that the process becomes economic. However there is little waste of material in the process and the parts taken from the mould are finished products.

Foam plastic components can be produced by injection moulding, inert gases being dissolved in the molten polymer. When the polymer cools the gases come out of solution and expand to form a cellular structure. A solid skin is produced where the molten polymer comes into contact initially with the cold mould surface. Typical products are stacking containers, toughened polystyrene tables and other office items.

Compression moulding and transfer moulding are used with thermosetting polymers. In compression moulding (*Figure 3.2*) the powdered polymer is compressed between the two parts of the mould and heated under this pressure. With transfer moulding (*Figure 3.3*) the powdered polymer is heated in a chamber before being transferred by a plunger into the mould, a process not unlike injection moulding.

The costs of moulds used with compression moulding tend to be lower than those used for either injection or transfer moulding, this is because the mould is simpler with no access for the molten polymer having to be left. With compression moulding inserts may present a problem, being damaged or moved when the pressure is applied. Transfer moulding does however allow complex parts with inserts to be readily made.

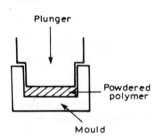

Figure 3.2 Compression moulding

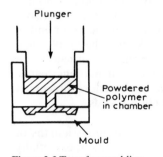

Figure 3.3 Transfer moulding

Compression moulding is used to produce products such as washing machine agitators, electrical plug cases, switch cases, knobs, car instrument panels, etc.

3 Extrusion

With the extrusion process, molten polymer is forced through a die. This is done by a screw mechanism which takes the polymer through a heated zone before forcing it through the die (*Figure 3.4*). The operation is continuous with a steady source of molten polymer being forced through the die. Long lengths of constant cross-section are produced. The process is used with thermoplastics for the production of pipes and various profiles such as curtain rails, sealing strips and skirting boards.

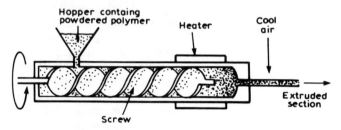

Figure 3.4 Extrusion

If thin film is required, a die can be used which gives an extruded cylinder of the material. This cylinder while still hot is inflated by compressed air to give a sleeve of thin film. An alternative method is to use a slit die and allow the hot material issuing from the die to fall vertically into a cooling system. This may be a water bath or a pair of cooled rollers. The film produced by either of these methods is used for packaging and a variety of decorative and office uses.

Sheet can be extruded by using a horizontal die of the appropriate shape. Such sheet may be used in secondary processing, such as thermoforming, to form products such as dinghy hulls and containers. Corrugated sheet produced this way is used for roofing.

With extrusion coating, a thin film of polymer is extruded from a slit die, drawn down to the required thickness and then pressed into contact with the required substrate. High coating speeds are possible, though the initial capital cost is high.

An important extrusion process is extrusion blow moulding. This process is used for the production of hollow articles, particularly plastic bottles. The operation involves extruding a hollow tube. A mould is placed round the hot tube, known as a parison, and closed up on it (*Figure 3.5*). The mould seals the lower end of the tube and the top end is cut off with a knife. The mould then moves on to have air injected into the parison. The air causes the still hot parison to fill the cold mould where it hardens before being ejected when the mould is opened. The entire process is automated and is capable of high production speeds.

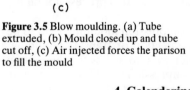

Figure 3.5 Blow moulding. (a) Tube extruded, (b) Mould closed up and tube cut off, (c) Air injected forces the parison to fill the mould

4 Calendering

This process is used for the production of continuous lengths of sheet thermoplastic materials. The calender consists of essentially three or more heated rollers (*Figure 3.6*). The heated polymer

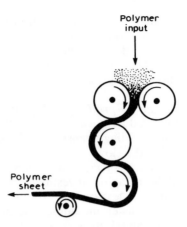

Figure 3.6 Calendering

passes between and round rollers to emerge as an output of sheet. The process is continuous.

5 Forming

Forming processes are secondary processes in that they are used to form articles from sheet polymer. The heated sheet is pressed into or around a mould. *Figure 3.7* illustrates one form of this process, this version being known as vacuum forming in that a reduction in air pressure between the sheet and the mould is used to cause the sheet to adopt the shape of the mould. With pressure moulding an increase in pressure is used on one side of the sheet in order to force the sheet to adopt the shape of the mould. With matched moulds forming, the heated sheet is formed by pressing between a pair of matched male and female moulds.

Thermoforming can have a reasonable output rate, but dimensional accuracy is not too good and holes and threads are not possible. The method can be used with very large sheets and is used for forming machine housings, pallets, car bodies, dinghy hulls, and small items such as drinking cups for vending machines, egg cartons and margarine tubs. The moulds may be made out of wood, metal or plaster. Mould costs can be relatively cheap.

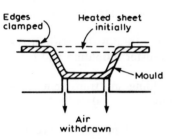

Figure 3.7 Vacuum forming

6 Machining

In the production of many products, machining can be avoided by a careful design and choice of the manufacturing process used. Conventional machining processes can be used with polymers but there are some problems associated with the facts that polymers are poor heat conductors and have low melting or degradation temperatures.

Because of the poor heat conduction, little of the heat developed during the machining operation is conducted away through the material. Thus the tool used tends to run very hot. Also the polymer, if a thermoplastic, tends to soften, swell and bind against the tool. This results in yet more friction and heat development, as well as tool wear. Hence, in machining polymers, correct machining conditions are vital. Some polymer materials are brittle and so present problems during machining, shock loads having to be avoided if cracking is not to occur.

3.3 CHOOSING A PROCESS

Injection moulding and extrusion are the most widely used processes. Injection moulding is generally used for the mass production of small items, often with intricate shapes. Extrusion is used for products which are required in continuous lengths or which are fabricated from continuous length, constant cross-section, material. The following are some of the factors that are involved in choosing a process.

1 Rate of production Injection moulding has the highest rate, followed by blow moulding, then rotational moulding, compression moulding, transfer moulding and thermoforming, with casting being the slowest.

2 Capital investment required Injection moulding requires the highest capital investment, with extrusion and blow moulding requiring less capital. Rotational moulding, compression, moulding, transfer moulding, thermoforming and casting require the least capital investment.

3 Most economic production run Injection moulding, extrusion and blow moulding are economic only with large production runs. Thermoforming, rotational moulding, casting and machining are used for the small production runs.

4 Surface finish Injection moulding, blow moulding, rotational moulding, thermoforming, transfer and compression moulding, and casting all give very good surface finishes. Extrusion gives only a good finish.

5 Metal inserts, during the process These are possible with injection moulding, rotational moulding, transfer moulding and casting.

6 Dimensional accuracy Injection moulding and transfer moulding are very good. Compression moulding good with casting; extrusion is fairly poor.

7 Very small items Injection moulding and machining are the best.

8 Enclosed hollow shapes Blow moulding and rotational moulding can be used.

9 Intricate, complex shapes Injection moulding, blow moulding, transfer moulding and extrusion.

10 Threads Injection moulding, blow moulding, casting and machining.

11 Large formed sheets Thermoforming.

Design considerations when using polymers

Polymers are not direct substitutes for metals and a component design that was a good one with a metal may be a bad one if a polymer is used instead of the metal. Polymers behave differently under load, there is a higher rate of creep, they are more affected by temperature changes, etc. The main advantages of polymers is that fairly accurate components can be produced, with an excellent surface finish and in colour, at a fairly low cost and at high production rates.

In a process involving the casting of metals or the casting or moulding of polymers essentially the same design considerations prevail. They are the problems associated with introducing a fluid or semifluid into a mould. The right amount of fluid has to be introduced and the mould must be completely filled without any air trapped in the mould. The design must therefore ensure that there is a free flow of the fluid to all parts of the mould and that air cannot become trapped. As with metals polymers shrink when they cool and solidify. Thus allowances have to be made for such

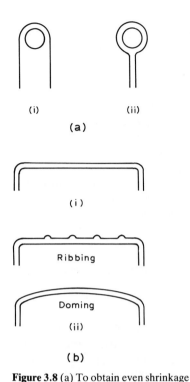

(i)　　　　　　(ii)

(a)

(i)

Ribbing

Doming

(ii)

(b)

Figure 3.8 (a) To obtain even shrinkage and less distortion (ii) is preferred to (i) (b) For more rigidity (ii) are preferred to (i)

shrinkage when the mould is designed. Also in designing the mould care has to be taken to ensure that the component can be removed from the mould, this means the product having a taper, generally of the order of a few degrees.

Thinner wall sections cool more rapidly than thicker wall sections, also the thicker sections shrink more than the thinner sections. Thus distortion can occur where there are changes in wall thickness. For this reason wall thicknesses should be kept as constant as possible. This generally means keeping walls fairly thin. Extra stiffness can be provided without increasing wall thickness by the use of ribs, flanges or webs (*Figure 3.8a*).

Polymers have low values for the modulus of elasticity and so large flat areas of sheet tend to easily bend and thus are difficult to keep rigid. The sheet can be made considerably more rigid, without increasing its thickness, by the use of ribbing or doming (*Figure 3.8b*).

Threads, either external or internal, can generally be moulded into the component. However such threads are generally not very hard wearing and it may be preferable, if frequent assembly and disassembly is required, to use an insert. Inserts can be moulded-in during the production of the component or introduced during later assembly by just push-fitting the insert, while hot, into the polymer. In either method care has to be taken that the insert does not pull out of the component when in service—it is only held by a mechanical bond. For this reason inserts may be knurled or grooved. Screwdriver blades are inserts into a plastic handle. So as to give a good grip when the handle is rotated the metal part in the handle is usually winged or flattened.

QUESTIONS

(1) How do thermosetting materials differ in properties from thermoplastics?

(2) Explain the principles of the rotational moulding process and state types of products that can be produced by this process.

(3) How does compression moulding differ from transfer moulding? What is the main effect of the difference on the type of mould that can be used?

(4) State two properties of polymers that significantly affect the way they can be machined.

(5) Suggest processes suitable for the following:
(a) High production rate required for a small plastic toy to be made from a thermoplastic material.
(b) A 1 litre bottle for soft drink, a thermoplastic material to be used. High production rates are required.
(c) A switch cover in a thermosetting material, as high a production rate as possible being required.
(d) Milk churns, about 340 mm diameter and 760 mm high, from polyethylene.
(e) A thermoplastic strip for use as a draught excluder with windows, long lengths being required.
(f) Mass production of polythene bags.
(g) The body for a camera, fairly high production rates being required.
(h) Mass production of the bodywork for an electric drill, threaded holes are needed.
(i) A nylon gear wheel, a high production rate being required.

4 Quality

After working through this chapter you should be able to:

Estimate the order of accuracy possible from a process.
Discuss the effect on costs of accuracy.
Recognise that all processes have variability in their output and identify some potential causes of such variability.
Explain how process capability can be established.
Explain how the minimum overall production cost can be established.
Explain what is meant by selective assembly.
Explain the interaction between design quality and production quality.

4.1 ACCURACY

In general, the more accuracy that is required for a component produced by a particular process the more it will cost, though for a particular accuracy some processes are more expensive than others. *Figure 4.1* shows the general relationship that exists between cost and accuracy.

With any process there is a technological limit to the accuracy that can be achieved and the nearer a process is used to that limit the more it will cost. Generally for a particular process there is a range of accuracy within which it is economic to use that process. *Figure 2.48* (page 44) shows cost/accuracy graphs for various machine and hand processes. The following table indicates the orders of highest accuracy which are economic with common manufacturing processes.

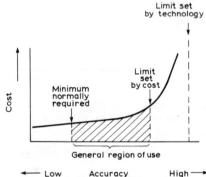

Figure 4.1 The cost of accuracy

Process	Tolerance/mm
Sand casting*	0.1
High pressure die casting*	0.05
Investment casting*	0.03
Closed die forging	0.2
Extrusion	0.1
Impact extrusion	0.05
Piercing/blanking	0.08
Powder techniques	0.002
Drilling	0.05
Planing/shaping	0.025
Milling	0.025
Turning	0.0125
Grinding	0.002
Chemical machining	0.075
Electrochemical machining	0.05
Electrodischarge machining	0.02

*On 100 mm size

The cost of accuracy On some products it may be a simple matter for the designer to change the tolerance. However, this could change the costs by a considerable amount because of the costs of producing the product to that tolerance. To illustrate this effect, consider the following example. This is based on data presented in the Manual of British Standards in *Engineering Drawing and Design* (1984) published by the British Standards Association, in association with Hutchinson.

Consider the production of an external diameter on a bore that can be revolved, the machine tool normally used being a turret, chuck or centre lathe with finishing by an external grinder. The costs are on the basis of 200 pieces in batches of 10. With such tools the normal commercial tolerance is 0.013 mm, the limit of machine shop equipment being 0.005 mm and the limit with special equipment being 0.003 mm (these are for up to 15 mm diameter). If, for instance, the existing tolerance is 0.15 mm then a change to a tolerance of 0.075 mm would increase the cost by a factor of 1.20. If the tolerance is changed to 0.01 mm then the cost increases by a factor of 4.01. A change to a tolerance of 0.003 mm increases the cost by a factor of 11.6. Thus changes in tolerances can have a profound impact on the cost of manufacturing the product, particularly when it goes beyond normal commercial tolerance limits.

The above cost took into account the time taken to produce the element concerned, including setting time and overhead charges; the cost or production and inspection gauges, any specialised tools and fixtures, the cost of any inspection in excess of normal, the cost of any additional operations required and a scrap allowance.

4.2 PROCESS VARIABILITY

The output from any machine or process will vary in accuracy due to a number of causes. These might be, tool and die wear, variations in the materials used, variations in the plant used, variations due to the labour used, variations in the environmental conditions, e.g. temperature, and the variations that might be expected because humans and imperfect machines are involved.

Thus, for example, in a deep drawing operation, the specific causes of variation might be die wear or the properties of the material. In a turning operation the variability might be due to the quality of the machine and labour used, as well as the machineability of the material and tool wear.

Process capability Suppose we take fifty successive components, as produced by some process or machine, and measure them. The measurements might take the following form (data in mm):

20.01	20.00	19.99	19.97	20.01	20.00	19.99	19.98	20.01	20.00
20.00	19.97	19.99	19.98	19.99	20.00	20.01	20.00	20.01	19.99
19.98	20.01	20.00	20.00	19.99	19.97	20.03	20.02	19.98	19.99
20.00	20.02	20.01	19.99	19.97	19.98	19.99	20.00	20.01	20.02
20.00	19.99	19.99	19.98	20.01	20.00	19.99	20.00	20.00	19.99

One way to see the type of variation that is occurring in the above process is to plot a frequency distribution curve. This means grouping the data and counting the number of readings that occur in each group, hence the frequency of occurrence. Thus in the

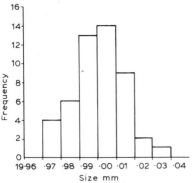

Figure 4.2 A histogram showing process variability

above case we might count the number of 20.00 mm readings, it is 14. The number of 19.99 mm readings is 13. What we are doing is finding the frequency with which the dimensions of the component occur within ± 0.005 mm of the reading quoted. *Figure 4.2* shows the resulting histogram. The pattern that can be discerned from the histogram is that most of the components have measurements of 19.99 or 20.00 mm.

Suppose for the component the nominal size required is 20.00 mm with a tolerance of 0.03 mm. This means that the acceptable components are those with dimensions between 20.03 and 19.97 mm. The histogram indicates that there are no components falling outside these limits and so all components are acceptable.

If more components had been measured and the readings taken to more decimal places, then the histogram would have approximated to a smooth curve, this being known as the frequency distribution curve. *Figure 4.3* shows some examples of such curves.

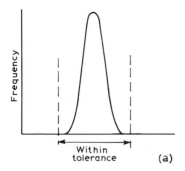 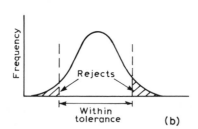 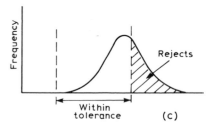

Figure 4.3 Frequency distribution curves. (a) No rejects, all components within the tolerance band. (b) Some rejects as some components are outside the tolerance band. (c) Some rejects, probably because the process is incorrectly set

In *Figure 4.3a*, all the components are within the tolerance band and so there are no rejects, the variability of the process being acceptable. In *Figure 4.3b*, some of the components are outside the tolerance band and so are rejected. The reasons for this excessive variability where there are as many components below the lower tolerance limit as above the upper tolerance limit would not be some factor which was consistently incorrect, such as an incorrect adjustment, because that would give a distribution curve more like *Figure 4.3c*. The reason might be play occurring in a bearing or the material machined being of variable quality. The distribution curve in *Figure 4.3c*, where there are a large number of rejects above the upper tolerance limit and none below the lower tolerance limit, could be explained either by a tool being out of alignment, or the machine setting was incorrectly set, or a new operator was using the machine, etc.

Mean and standard deviation   An alternative to drawing the frequency distribution curves is to calculate for the measured components the mean and the standard deviation values. The mean, or average, value is obtained by adding together all the measurements and dividing by the number of measurements made. Thus, for the fifty components measured and results given in the previous section in this chapter, the sum of all the measured values is 999.81 mm and hence the mean is 999.81/50 = 19.996 mm, or to the accuracy with which the measurements were made 20.00 mm. This mean being at the nominal value would indicate that the situation is not like the distribution shown in *Figure 4.3c* and that, though there may be variations, there is no systematic reason, such as a wrong machine setting, for them. What the mean value does not give information about is the amount of variation within the measurements. Thus, for example, the mean values for *Figures 4.3a* and *4.3b* are the same but *Figure 4.3b* has obviously more variability than *Figure 4.3a*. A measure of this variability is given by the standard deviation.

For a sample size of *n* components measured, where $\bar{x}$ is the mean value and *x* the value of one of the measurements, then the standard deviation is given by

$$\text{standard deviation} = \sqrt{\frac{\Sigma(x - \bar{x})^2}{n}}$$

The standard deviation is therefore calculated by adding together all the squares of the differences between the measured values and the mean value, dividing the resultant sum by the total number of measurements, and then taking the square root of the result.

The following table illustrates how the standard deviation is calculated for the data given in the previous section, where the mean value was found to be 20.00 mm.

x/mm	$(x - \bar{x})$/mm	$(x - \bar{x})^2$/mm^2
20.01	0.01	0.0001
20.00	0	0
19.99	−0.01	0.0001
19.97	−0.03	0.0009
20.01	0.01	0.0001
20.00	0	0
19.99	0.01	0.0001
19.98	−0.02	0.0004
20.01	0.01	0.0001
20.00	0	0

etc for the full fifty measurements.

Then the sum of all the values of $(x - \bar{x})^2$ is obtained, in this case for the fifty measurements the sum is 0.0103 mm^2. This is then divided by the total number of observations 0.0103/50 = 0.000206 mm^2 and then the square root obtained to give the standard deviation of 0.014 mm.

The frequency distribution curves for many processes approximate to what is called a normal distribution. For such a distribution a knowledge of the standard deviation, σ, enables us to state the number of measurements that would be within, or outside, any limits we put on the curve, e.g. the tolerance value.

Limits	*Percentage outside these limits*
Mean ± 1.0σ	31.7
Mean ± 1.5σ	13.4
Mean ± 2.0σ	4.55
Mean ± 2.5σ	1.24
Mean ± 3.0σ	0.27
Mean ± 3.09σ	0.20

Thus for the sample considered where the mean is 20.00 mm and the standard deviation 0.014 mm, then 13.4% of the sample would be expected to be outside $20.00 \pm 1.5 \times 0.014 = 20.021$ mm. If the tolerance had been 0.021 mm then 13.4% of the sample would have been outside the tolerance limits and so rejected. For practical purposes the curve is assumed to stop at 3.09σ, the percentage of components having measurements outside that limit being 0.20% and generally considered to be insignificant. Hence for the example considered, if the tolerance was greater than $3.09\sigma = 3.09 \times 0.014 = 0.043$ mm then the entire sample considered could be considered to be within tolerance.

Selecting a process Suppose we have the situation where a finished component is required to have a nominal length of 20 mm with a tolerance of 0.01 mm. A consideration of the process proposed shows that it produces components with a mean length of 20 mm and a standard deviation of 0.014 mm. This would mean that if that process alone was used we have a tolerance limit which is just about one standard deviation and so we could expect a rejection rate of the order of 31.7%

In order to reduce the rejection rate we could introduce a second process in order to bring more of the components within the required tolerance or take another look at the process proposed.

4.3   MINIMUM OVERALL PRODUCTION COST Costs are involved whenever products fail to meet the required tolerances and therefore are not of the required quality. We can assume two elements to this cost, the failure cost and the cost of appraising that, after the product has been made, only those of the required quality are sold to the customer. The cost of failure includes:
The cost of the product that has to be thrown away;
The cost of reworking that is needed to bring it within the required tolerance;
The cost of the production capacity lost to useful production;

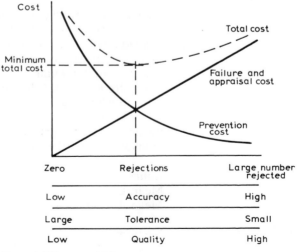

Figure 4.4 The cost of failure

The interference with the production schedule;

The labour costs involved in finding the reasons for the failure and rectifying it;

Possibly costs incurred because the customer becomes dissatisfied because the products have not been produced on schedule, etc.

The total failure and appraisal cost can be expected to be higher according to the greater the number of rejected products. If there are no rejects then the cost of failure and appraisal will be zero. *Figure 4.4* shows, for one of its graph lines, how the cost of failure and appraisal might be expected to change with the number of rejections. As the number of rejections will depend on the accuracy required, i.e. the tolerance specified, then the failure and appraisal cost can also be considered to depend on those factors.

Figure 4.4 also shows a prevention cost factor. This is the money which is spent to ensure that products are not made that will be rejected by virtue of not meeting the required tolerance. Such a cost might involve, for example, the cost of inspection during manufacture, maintenance of machines so that they can consistently produce the required quality, training for the workforce so that they become skilled in producing the required quality, etc. When the rejection rate is high then we might consider that the costs of prevention must have been low. When there are few rejects then it seems reasonable to assume that prevention costs will be high. For such reasons we, therefore, can expect that when the failure and appraisal cost is low then the prevention cost is high, and vice versa.

Therefore, the total cost of production can be considered to be made up of the two cost factors, the failure and appraisal cost and the prevention cost. At some particular number of rejections the total cost is a minimum. Crude though this graph is, the important point that it demonstrates is that there is a minimum number of rejections below which it is not economic to go.

Selective assembly

One method of assembling components is to take any one component, say a shaft, from a batch and fit it to any one component from a batch of, say, sleeves. This assumes that the tolerances on both components can be held well enough for the two to fit together with no problems. This can mean that very tight tolerances have to be maintained for both components. A consequence of this is that there might be a high reject rate for the two components because the variability that is inherent within any process might be such as to give some of the components outside the tolerance limits.

In order to reduce the rejection rate, by increasing the width of the tolerance band within which components will be accepted, selective assembly can be used. This means matching together the two components being assembled so that two are selected that fit together. This involves grading the output of the component so that it is possible to choose from a batch a component with, say, dimensions on the high side, perhaps in a particular range of dimensions. Such a technique can reduce scrap levels and reworking costs.

The quality of conformance

The quality of any manufactured item can be considered under two headings—the quality of design and the quality of conformance. The quality of design is the quality specified by the designer;

the quality of conformance is the quality produced by the manufacture of the item. This quality of conformance can be considered
to be the extent to which the manufactured item complies with the
designer's specifications, i.e. the degree to which it conforms.
There can be a gap between the quality specified by the designer
and the quality that the production department can deliver.

In designing a product, the designer will consider the customer's
requirements. Though the designer may be able to produce a
design which gives the quality required by the customer there may
be a problem in that the product cannot be manufactured to that
quality, or more likely may not be capable of being manufactured
to that quality at the required cost. In other words, there is a gap
between the quality of design and the quality of conformance. For
example, the customer may want a Rolls Royce. The designer
produces a design for one but the production department may not
be able to produce a car to the Rolls Royce specification because
they perhaps do not have the appropriate skilled labour or the
tools or perhaps the customer wanted the Rolls Royce at the price
of a Mini and the production department just could not produce
the Rolls Royce at that cost.

Though this may seem to be rather an absurd example, consider
the information presented earlier in this chapter concerning the
relationship between cost and accuracy, the greater the accuracy
required the greater the cost. Thus though the customer may want
a product to a high accuracy and this is designed to the required
accuracy, the production department may not be able to manufacture the item to that accuracy at the required cost. There may, for
instance, be a high rejection rate for the products manufactured in
order that the accuracy to the customer is maintained.

The input to the designer is the customer's requirements for the
product. There has also, however, to be an input from the
production department on the capabilities and cost implications of
the different manufacturing processes and also an input of information on the properties of the materials that might be chosen
and their costs. Only by considering all these factors is it possible
for the designer to produce a design which stands a chance of being
produced at the required quality, in other words having a quality
of design and a quality of conformance that are the same.

QUESTIONS

(1) Rank the following processes in order of highest to lowest
accuracy that is economic with the processes—closed die
forging, powder techniques, milling.

(2) Extrusion or turning can be used to produce a particular
section, which process would be capable of the greatest
accuracy?

(3) The following sequence of questions is based on data given in
the Manual of British Standards in *Engineering Drawing and
Design* (1984) published by the British Standards Association
in association with Hutchinson.

For 200 pieces in batches of 10, the cost of the accuracy of
an internal diameter on a bore that can be revolved is
increased by the following factors if the existing tolerance

was 0.075 mm:

Proposed tolerance/mm	0.04	0.02	0.01	0.005
Cost factor	1.34	1.71	3.58	8.10

The machine tool normally used is the turret, chuck or centre lathe and an internal grinder. The normal commercial tolerance on a diameter up to 150 mm is 0.025 mm, the limit of the general machine shop equipment is 0.01 mm and the limit with special equipment is 0.005 mm.

(a) If the cost of producing an internal diameter was £20 when the tolerance was 0.075 mm, what will be the cost if the tolerance is changed to 0.01 mm?

(b) Why does the cost rise when increased accuracy is required?

(c) Why does the change to a tolerance of 0.005 mm give a much greater change in cost than a change to 0.01 mm?

(4) Identify some important causes of process variability.

(5) Quality costs can be divided into three categories: failure, appraisal and prevention costs. Explain these terms.

(6) Sketch the form of the frequency distribution curve when for an inspected sample (a) all the products tested fell within the tolerance band, (b) due to random causes some fell outside the tolerance band, (c) an incorrect setting of the machine was used and it produced goods at sizes having a mean greater than the nominal size and some fell outside the tolerance band.

(7) A product is required with a tolerance of 0.01 mm. An investigation of the process used shows that the variability has a mean that coincides with the nominal value and a standard deviation of 0.005 mm. What percentage of the products would you expect to be unacceptable?

(8) A process is found to have a standard deviation of 0.01 mm about the nominal value. What tolerance would be feasible if there was to be no more than about 1¼% of the products outside the tolerance band?

(9) Explain why minimum production costs may occur when there are some products which are outside the tolerance band and so are rejected.

(10) What is meant by selective assembly?

(11) What is meant by the terms quality of design and quality of conformance?

(12) What problems can occur if there is a difference between the quality of design and the quality of conformance?

5 Assembly operations

After working through this chapter you should be able to:

State the basic principles, the characteristics and the limitations of the basic assembly methods for metals of (a) adhesives, (b) soldering and brazing, (c) welding, and (d) fastening systems.
State the basic principles, the characteristics and the limitations of the basic assembly methods for plastics of (a) welding, (b) adhesive bonding, (c) riveting, (d) press and snap fits, (e) thread systems.
Recognise the need for an assembly breakdown and factors which make for easier and faster assembly.
Explain the basic principles of mechanised and automated assembly.
Use the terminology associated with limits and fits and the ISO system.

5.1 ASSEMBLY PROCESSES FOR METALS

The main processes used for assembly can be summarised as:
1 *Adhesive bonding* The types of adhesives used could be natural adhesives, elastomers, thermoplastics, thermosets and two-polymer types.
2 *Soldering and brazing* The joining agent used is different from the two materials being joined but alloys locally with them.
3 *Welding* Heat or pressure is used to fuse the two materials being joined together.
4 *Fastening systems* Fasteners provide a clamping force between the two pieces of materials being joined, e.g. nuts and bolts, rivets.

5.2 ADHESIVES FOR METALS

The use of adhesives to bond materials together can have advantages over other joining methods, i.e.

(a) Dissimilar materials can be joined, e.g. metals to polymers;
(b) Jointing can take place over large areas;
(c) A uniform distribution of stress over the entire bonded area is produced—with a minimum of stress concentration;
(d) The bond is generally permanent;
(e) Jointing can be carried out at room temperature or temperatures close to it;
(f) Gives a smooth finish.

Disadvantages are that optimum bond strength is usually not produced immediately; a curing time has to be allowed. The bond can be affected by environmental factors such as heat, cold and humidity. These adhesives generally cannot be used at temperatures above about 200°C.

Adhesives can be classified according to the type of chemical involved. The main types are as follows:

1 Natural adhesives Vegetable glues made from plant starches are typical examples of natural adhesives. These types are used on postage stamps and envelopes. However, such adhesives give bonds with poor strength which are susceptible to fungal attack and are also weakened by moisture. They set as a result of solvent evaporation.

2 Elastomers Elastomeric adhesives are based on synthetic rubbers; they also set as a result of solvent evaporation. Strong joints are not produced as these have low shear strength. The adhesive is inclined to creep. These adhesives are mainly used for unstressed joints and flexible bonds with plastics and rubbers.

3 Thermoplastics These include a number of different setting types. An important group are those, such as polyamides, which are applied hot, solidify and bond on cooling. They are widely used with metals, plastics, wood, etc and have a wide application in rapid assembly work such as furniture assembly and the production of plastic film laminates.

Another group are the acrylic acid diesters which set when air is excluded, the reaction being one of a build-up of molecular chain length. Cyanoacrylates, the 'super-glues' set in the presence of moisture, in a similar way, with the reaction taking place in seconds. This makes them very useful for rapid assembly of small components. Other forms of thermoplastic adhesives set by solvent evaporation, e.g. polyvinyl acetate.

In general, thermoplastic adhesives have a low shear strength and under high loads are subject to creep, so they are generally used in assemblies subject to low stresses. They have poor to good resistance to water but good resistance to oil.

4 Thermosets These set as a result of a build-up of molecular chains to give a rigid cross-linked matrix. Epoxy resins, such as Araldite, are one of the most widely used thermset adhesives. These are two-part adhesives, in that setting only starts to occur when the two parts are brought together. They will bond almost anything and give strong bonds which are resistant to water, oil and solvents.

Phenolic resins are another example of thermoset adhesives. Heat and pressure are necessary for setting. They have good strength and resistance to water, oil and solvents and are widely used for bonding plywood.

5 Two-polymer types Thermosets by themselves give brittle joints, but combined with a thermoplastic or elastomer a more flexible joint can be produced. Phenolic resins with nitrile or neoprene rubbers have high shear strength, excellent peal strength, good resistance to water, oils and solvents and good creep properties. Phenolic resins with polyvinyl acetate, a thermoplastic, give similar bond strengths but with even better resistance to water, oils and solvents. These adhesives are used for bonding laminates and metals. Joints using them can be subject to high stresses and can often operate satisfactorily up to temperatures around 200°C.

For the maximum strength bonds to be realised with an adhesive, the maximum area of bonding should be used. *Figure 5.1* shows some typical joints.

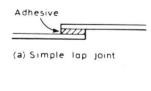

(a) Simple lap joint

(b) Bevelled lap joint

(c) Rebated lap joint

Figure 5.1 Adhesive joints

5.3   SOLDERING AND BRAZING

Soldering involves heating the joining agent, the solder, together with the materials being joined until the solder melts and alloys with their surfaces. On cooling, the alloy solidifies and forms a bond between the two materials. The joining process requires temperatures below about 425° and often below 300°C.

Solders are only weak structural materials when compared with the metals they generally join; thus there is a need to ensure that the strength of the soldered joint does not rely on solder strength and is designed so that preferably the materials interlock or overlap in some way (*Figure 5.2*). The hot solder must wet the surfaces being joined otherwise it will not alloy with them. Preparation of the surfaces is thus vital, generally involving abrasion, degreasing and the use of a flux. Fluxes, when heated, promote or accelerate the wetting of the surfaces by the solder. They remove oxide layers from both metal and solder and prevent them reforming during soldering.

Brazing is a process similar to soldering but involves temperatures above 425°C, but below the melting points of the materials being joined. The term 'braze' derives from the fact that brass is used to make the joint. However, nowadays, other alloys are also used. Like soldering it is preferable for the materials to interlock or overlap in some way, so that the joint is designed for shear rather than direct tension. *Figure 5.3* shows some of the joint forms that are preferable with brazing. Brazing gives stronger joints than soldering.

Single overlap joint

(a)

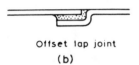

Offset lap joint

(b)

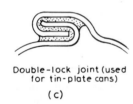

Double-lock joint (used for tin-plate cans)

(c)

Figure 5.2 Solder joints

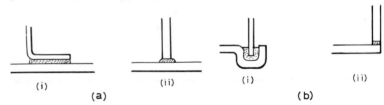

(i)   (ii)   (i)   (ii)

(a)   (b)

Figure 5.3 So that the joints are in shear (i) is preferred in each case to (ii). (a) A T junction. (b) A corner

5.4   WELDING METALS

With brazing and soldering, the joint is effected by inserting a metal between the two surfaces being joined, the inserted metal having a lower melting point than that of the materials being joined. With welding, the joint is effected directly between the parts being joined by the application of heat or pressure. In fusion welding an external heat source is used to melt the interfaces of the joint materials and so cause the materials to fuse together. With solid state welding, pressure is used to bring the two interfaces into intimate contact and so fuse the two materials together.

With adhesive bonded, soldered or welded joints there needs to be an overlap of the materials at the joints in order that the joint material is in shear rather than direct tension. This is because the joint material is weaker than the materials that are joined and is necessary to achieve the maximum strength. This is not the case with welding. The two materials being joined are fused together and so the material at the joint is the same as the parent material. Hence there is no need for an overlap, butt joints can be made and are strong (*Figure 5.4*).

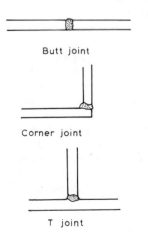

Butt joint

Corner joint

T joint

Figure 5.4 Weld joints

Welding is capable of producing high strength joints. However, because of the high temperatures involved, there may be detrimental changes in the materials being joined. There may also be local distortions due to uneven thermal expansion, residual stresses, or micro-structural changes. There are a large number of different welding processes, however they can be grouped into five main types.

1 Solid phase

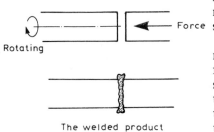

Figure 5.5 Friction welding

Cold pressure welding uses mechanical deformation at room temperature to bring the two materials into intimate contact and so fuse them together. It is however only applicable to ductile metals such as aluminium or copper. Hot pressure welding is similar but uses heat to make the material more ductile.

Explosive welding uses explosive charges to impact the two materials together and fuse their interfaces. It is a useful technique for joining dissimilar materials. Friction welding has the two surfaces rubbing together (*Figure 5.5*) in order to clean them and to provide heat as a result of friction. Generally the parts joined by this process are cylindrical. With diffusion welding (or bonding) the workpieces are held together under light pressure and heated to a temperature which is sufficiently high to cause atoms to diffuse across the boundary between the two materials, the operation taking place in a vacuum. Dissimilar metals may be joined by this process.

2 Thermochemical

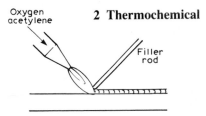

Figure 5.6 Oxyacetylene welding

The heat to fuse the metals together is provided by a gas flame, usually acetylene and oxygen burnt in a torch (*Figure 4.6*), or by an exothermic chemical reaction producing liquid metal which is poured into the joint. The exothermic reaction is provided by iron oxide and aluminium being ignited and producing liquid iron. Oxyacetylene welding is a low cost, portable, operation usually used for quick machine repairs and small miscellaneous jobs with mainly ferrous alloys up to about 8 mm thick.

3 Electric-resistance

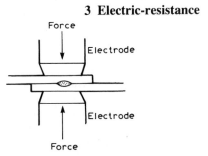

Figure 5.7 Spot welding

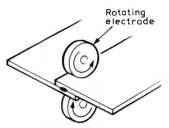

Figure 5.8 Seam welding

In this case the heat needed to fuse the metals together is provided either by the passage of an electric current across the interface of the joint, or the current is induced by electromagnetic induction in the metal near the joint. Widely used types of resistance welding are spot welding, seam welding and projection welding. Spot welding is used for joining sheet metal and involves squeezing the two sheets between a pair of electrodes (*Figure 5.7*). When a current is passed between the electrodes a molten nugget of metal is produced at the interface between the two sheets which rapidly solidifies when the current ceases. The process is widely used for high speed mass production operations with steel sheets up to 3 mm thick.

Seam welding is similar to spot welding but instead of cylindrical electrodes copper alloy wheel electrodes are used. These rotate and drive the workpiece through the machine during the welding operation (*Figure 5.8*). The appearance of the weld is that of a series of overlapping spot welds or spots spaced at regular intervals, the motion of the wheels and the current pulsing being adjustable.

With spot and seam welding the current is made to flow through just one small area by the pressure from the electrodes forcing the

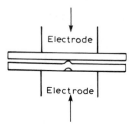

Figure 5.9 Projection welding

sheets into intimate contact at those points, hence it is only at these points that the welding occurs. With projection welding the current is made to flow through just one small area by small projections raised on one of the sheets (*Figure 5.9*). During welding, the projections collapse as a result of the heat and pressure and the sheets are brought into close contact. This process is versatile and can be used for joining any two shapes, provided a contact point is possible where the weld is to be made. It is widely used for attaching small components, e.g. fasteners, to larger components.

4 Electric arc   Essentially three forms of electric arc welding occur, the distinction between them being the method adopted to protect the hot metal from attack by the atmosphere and the cleaning away of contaminating surface films on the materials being joined, the term shielding being used to describe the process. There is the unshielded arc, the flux-shielded arc and the gas-shielded arc. Basically the process of arc welding, in whatever form of shielding, involves producing an arc between a metal electrode and the workpiece by passing a high current between them. Flux shielded arcs are probably the most widely used welding process.

With the metal arc version of flux-shielded arcs, the electric arc passes between a metal rod, called the core wire, which is covered with flux (*Figure 5.10*). The core wire melts and is transferred to the weld pool. Simultaneously the flux coating of the wire forms a molten slag which protects the liquid metal. In addition protective gases are also given off. This process is used mainly for welding steels, though can be used for other metals with the exception of aluminium alloys. It is used with thicknesses from the thin to very thick. The equipment costs are fairly low.

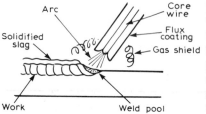

Figure 5.10 Metal arc welding

The submerged arc version of flux-shielded arc welding uses a continuous bare electrode wire with the shielding flux being supplied separately in powdered or granule form in a layer over the work area, submerging it. The process is used with steels in shipbuilding, structural and general engineering, for metal thicknesses from about 8 mm upwards.

With gas-shielded arcs the shielding is supplied by a continuous stream of gas over the work area. Tungsten inert-gas welding (TIG) uses an arc from a tungsten electrode in an atmosphere of argon of helium (*Figure 5.11*). Extra metal to fill the joint is supplied separately as the tungsten electrode is not consumed. High quality welds are produced, though the process is rather slow. Unlike flux-shielded arcs no cleaning up of the weld area is required after the welding. The process is mainly used for the welding of sheet materials.

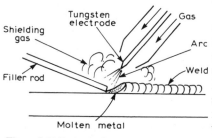

Figure 5.11 Tungsten inert-gas welding

Plasma arc welding is similar to tungsten inert-gas welding with the arc being passed through a small orifice in a water cooled nozzle before reaching the workpiece. Another version of gas-shielded arc welding is metal inert gas welding (MIG). In this version the arc is formed between a continuously fed electrode wire and the work, with a gas supply providing the shielding. The process is fairly costly and is used for the thicknesses from 0.5 mm upwards.

5 Radiant energy   In electron-beam welding a stream of electrons is produced and used to bombard the materials being welded, the result of the bombardment being the generation of heat. The entire operation is generally carried out in a vacuum. The process can produce very deep narrow welds. The equipment cost is fairly high.

Another radiant energy form of welding involves the use of a laser. Unlike electron-beam welding, the workpiece does not have to be in a vacuum. Both methods however are using focussed beams of energy. Because with lasers intense energy can be focussed down to a very small area, precision work is possible and high melting point metals welded which would be virtually impossible by other means. Thicknesses up to about 3 mm can be handled.

Selecting a welding process   The choice of welding process for a particular situation is determined by the following factors:

(a) The thickness of the materials being welded Thus, for instance, spot welding can be used for steels up to about 3 mm thick, and occasionally up to 6 mm. It cannot be used for thicker materials. Projection welding can also only be used for sheets up to about 3 mm thick. Submerged arc welding however is generally not suitable for materials thinner than about 8 mm.

(b) The joint shape If the ends of two steel rods are to be joined then friction welding is a possible method, however it would be unsuitable for a butt joint between the edges of two steel plates.

(c) The need for inspection The design of the joint must take into account the need for an inspection of the weld on its completion. The accessibility of the joint also affects the choice of the welding process to be used in that the welder must be able to get at the joint area in order to carry out the welding. Some processes are more easily adapted to awkward situations than others. For instance, the metal arc method only requires the electrode to be directed into the position, perhaps a corner.

(d) Whether the process is to be automatic. Where a large number of welds of a similar type or a long length of weld are involved, automatic processes, rather than manual methods, are generally to be preferred. Submerged arc welding can be used in this way. Metal arc welding would not be suitable because of the operator skill that is required to maintain the arc and the metal feed.

5.5 FASTENING SYSTEMS WITH METALS   The choice of fastener, from the very wide variety available, will depend on a number of factors:

(a) Environmental The conditions under which the fastener is to be used, e.g. temperature and corrosive conditions.

(b) Nature of the external loading on the fastener Different fasteners are appropriate for the different types of loading, e.g. tension, compression, shear, cyclic or impact, and the magnitude of the loading.

(c) Life and service requirements Is the fastener to be permanent or demountable? Is there to be frequent assembly and disassembly?

(d) The quantity of the fasteners required and their cost

(e) The method of assembly of the fastener This is often one of the

prime factors determining choice in that over 60% of the cost of using a fastener in an assembly is likely to be the assembly operator's handling time. It can be as high as 90%. Thus a choice of fastener which permits a short handling time can have a very significant effect on the overall cost.

Fasteners can be classified into three types—threaded, non-threaded and special-purpose. The purpose of a fastener, in all forms, is however to provide a clamping force between two pieces of material. Of the metals used, steel is probably the most common, although aluminium alloys, brass and nickel are among other metals used. Aluminium alloy fasteners have the advantage over steel of being much lighter, non-magnetic and more corrosion resistant. Nickel has the particular advantage of strength at high temperatures.

1 Threaded fasteners

With a threaded fastener, the clamping force holding the two pieces of material together is produced by a torque being applied to the fastener and being maintained during the service life of the fastener. Bolts mated with nuts, and screws with threads in the material, are examples of threaded fasteners.

The performance of a threaded fastener is affected by many factors, notably the thread form, the loading, the fastener material and the effect of coatings of the fastener material. Steel bolts, for instance, might be coated with zinc or cadmium to make them more resistant to corrosion.

2 Non-threaded fasteners

Examples of non-threaded fasteners are rivets, eyelets, pins and spring-retaining clips. Rivets can be used for joining dissimilar or similar materials, both metallic and non-metallic, to give permanent joints.

Figure 5.12 shows the basic stages that are typical of a riveting process. When the force applied to the rivet is sufficiently high

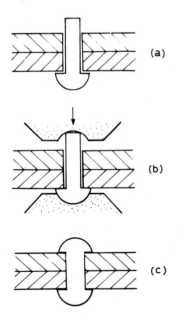

Figure 5.12 Typical stages in a riveting process

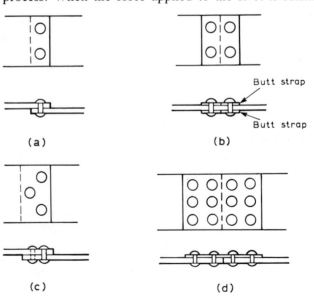

Figure 5.13 Riveted joints. (a) Single riveted lap joint. (b) Single riveted butt joint with two butt straps. (c) Double riveted lap joint. (d) Double riveted butt joint with a single butt strap

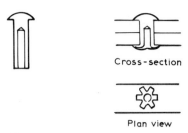

Cross-section

Plan view

Figure 5.14 A tubular rivet

Figure 5.15 A bifurcated rivet

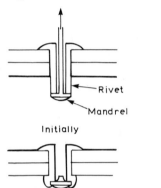

Rivet

Mandrel

Initially

Broken off
head of mandrel

Finally

Figure 5.16 A Pop rivet

The eyelet

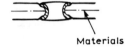

Materials

Cross-section of fixed eyelet

Figure 5.17 One form of eyelet

Figure 5.18 A taper pin

Figure 5.19 A cotter-pin joint

plastic deformation occurs and the shank of the rivet increases in diameter as its length decreases. That part of the shank within the hole increases in diameter until it fills the hole, the unsupported part of the shank outside of the hole continues to deform until a head is formed. A ductile material has to be used for the rivet material, e.g. mild steel, copper, brass, aluminium, aluminium alloys. For some materials the rivets are used in the cold state, in other cases they are used while hot.

Figure 5.13 shows some of the forms of riveted joints. In some cases butt straps, thin sheets of material between the rivet heads and the materials being joined, are used. Other applications use multiple rows of rivets. In applications where the riveting force might be large enough to damage or distort the materials being joined, tubular or semi-tubular rivets might be used instead of solid rivets (*Figure 5.14*).

Tubular rivets can, in some circumstances, be self-piercing. This means that a hole does not have to be drilled prior to inserting the rivet. Tubular rivets are, however, only limited to materials such as leather and fibre for self-piercing. Bifurcated rivets are used as self-piercing in a wider range of materials, e.g. plywood, plastics and fibres. *Figure 5.15* shows the type of form of such a rivet, such a rivet having just two prongs.

The term blind rivet is used for those rivets that are installed from just one side of the workpiece, requiring no other operator or holding tool on the other side. One form of such a rivet is the pop rivet. This consists of a hollow rivet assembled on a steel mandrel. When the rivet has been inserted into the hole in the workpiece a special tool is used to pull the mandrel and cause the hollow end of the rivet to expand on the blind side and so clamp the materials of the workpiece together (*Figure 5.16*). In some forms, the head of the mandrel breaks off and remains in the rivet to act as a plug, in other forms the head just breaks off and falls away to leave the centre of the rivet open.

The term 'eyelet' is given to a small item used as either a hole strengthener or as a light load fastener. *Figure 5.17* shows the basic form of an eyelet, consisting generally of a tubular body with a head at one end. It is inserted through the hole in the materials and pressure applied to deform the non-head end and form a head at that end, hence clamping the materials.

Pins, either in the solid or tubular forms, are widely used for fastening, and also hinges, pivots, etc. Thus taper pins (*Figure 5.18*) are used to join wheels on to the ends of shafts, the pin just being driven through holes in the two parts until it is fully home and a tight fit occurs. Another form of pin is the split cotter pin (*Figure 5.19*). This is used where freedom of movement in the joint is required or as a locking device for slotted nuts on bolts.

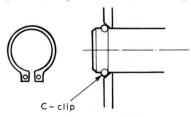

C-clip

Figure 5.20 A spring retaining clip

There is a wide variety of forms of spring-retaining clips. A simple form is a C-clip which is used to lock and retain components on shafts, the clip generally fitting into a groove on the shaft (*Figure 5.20*).

5.6 ASSEMBLY METHODS FOR PLASTICS

The assembly processes that can be used with plastics can be considered to fall into four groups:

1 Welding This process is similar to metal welding and involves using heat to fuse two thermoplastic materials together.
2 Adhesive bonding The types of adhesives used could be elastomers, thermoplastics, thermosets and two-polymer types.
3 Riveting Both metal and thermoplastic rivets are used.
4 Press and snap fits This is an important way of making both permanent and recoverable assemblies. Plastics can be distorted quite a considerable amount elastically and recover their original dimensions and shape afterwards. This is the basis of this type of assembly.
5 Thread systems Screw threads and self-tapping screws are widely used.

5.7 WELDING THERMOPLASTICS

There are nine method of welding thermoplastics:

Spin welding;   Ultrasonic welding;
Vibration welding;   Resistance-wire welding;
Hot-gas welding;   Dielectric welding;
Hot-plate welding;   Induction welding.
Hot-wire welding;

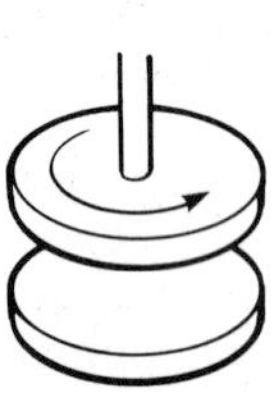

Spin welding and vibration welding (sometimes referred to as oscillatory welding) are friction welding methods in which the weld is produced by the frictional heat developed at the interface between the two thermoplastic materials. Spin welding is only suitable for circular components and involves holding the lower part in a jig while the upper part is brought into contact with it while rotating at high speed (*Figure 5.21*). The friction at the interface rapidly causes the plastic to melt and the surfaces then fuse together. This is a reliable method of producing pressure and vacuum-tight joints having a bond which is almost as strong as the parent material. Vibration welding can be applied to non-circular shapes, the method involving an oscillatory motion rather than a rotation as with spin welding, The effects are the same.

Hot-gas welding, hot-plate welding and hot-wire welding all involve the melting of the interface of the joint by direct heating. Hot-gas welding is similar to oxyacetylene welding of metals, involving heat being applied using a welding torch blowing hot gas on to the joint and a filler rod being used to supply molten plastic to fill the joint (*Figure 5.22*). The process requires a skilled operator if high strength joints are to be produced, too little heating of the joint area and the weld will be weak, too much heating and the plastic will degrade and a poor weld will be produced. This process is used for the fabrication of large containers.

Figure 5.21 The basis of spin-welding

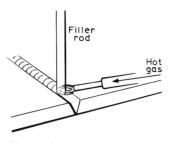

Figure 5.22 Hot-gas welding

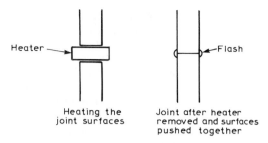

Heater ⟶

Flash

Heating the
joint surfaces

Joint after heater
removed and surfaces
pushed together

Figure 5.23 Hot plate welding

In hot-plate welding, the faces of the parts to be joined are pressed against a heated plate, coated with PTFE to prevent sticking, the plate is then withdrawn and the two surfaces to be joined pressed together (*Figure 5.23*). By using specially designed heaters, three-dimensional shapes can be welded by this method. Nylons cannot be welded this way since they oxidise when the melted resin is exposed to air. Hot-plate welding is used for the on-site joining of thermoplastic pipes.

Hot-wire welding involves constant pressure being applied to the joint while an electrically heated wire passes through the joint, melting the plastic and thus forming a weld.

Ultrasonic welding essentially involves an input to the joint area of high frequency vibrations, of the order of 20 kHz. These cause the two surfaces of the joint to vibrate against each other and, as a result of friction, melt. The process is fast, some machines being capable of bonding some 30 parts per minute by this method, and is capable of being automated. Weld strength is consistently high and the process is very versatile. Some thermoplastics cannot however be welded by this method.

Resistance wire welding involves passing a current through a wire which has been inserted in joint area. After the interfaces have melted and fused, the wire is left in position. This process has been used in the construction of the hulls of sailing craft.

Dielectric welding is used for the welding together of thin sheets of plastic. The materials are placed between the plates of a capacitor, acting as the dielectric. A high frequency alternating voltage is applied to the capacitor and the resulting high frequency electric field in the plastic causes heating and hence bonding. This process has been used for the production of upholstery, imitation leather, luggage and inflatables.

Induction welding involves inserting a strip of metal along the joint, in some cases this is a tape which is electrically conducting. No direct connections are made to this conductor but it is placed inside a coil through which an alternating current passes. Electromagnetic induction results in an e.m.f. being induced in the conductor and this causes local heating, hence melting of the plastic and so bonding.

5.8 ADHESIVE BONDING OF PLASTICS

The main types of adhesives used with plastics are epoxy resins, acryllic acid diesters, two-part acrylics and the cyanoacrylates.

Epoxy resins are thermosetting adhesives, see earlier in this chapter, and usually involve two components, the resin and the hardener, which have to be combined for the bond to be made.

Generally they are used with thermosetting materials, producing good bonds with those materials, but not so useful with thermoplastics in that poorer bonds are produced.

The acrylic acid diesters set when air is excluded, the term anaerobic often being used to indicate that they set without oxygen. The surfaces to be bonded are coated and then brought together under light pressure, this excluding air. They form good bonds with thermosets but are not suitable for use with the common engineering thermoplastics. Two-part acrylics involve a hardener being used with the acrylic resin, one surface of the joint being coated with hardener and the other with the resin. The two surfaces are then brought together for the bond to be made. These adhesives will bond to almost anything and are used with thermosets and many thermoplastics. The cyanoacrylates, the 'superglues', will form good bonds with thermosets and virtually all thermoplastics.

Some plastics can be bonded by the use of a solvent, nylons, polystyrene and PVC are examples of such plastics. The solvent is used to soften the interfaces of the joint and then light pressure applied to bring the surfaces in close contact.

5.9   RIVETING OF PLASTICS

Riveting using metal rivets can be used to make joints between plastics and between plastics and metals. Tubular or bifurcated rivets are generally used. The problem with riveting is that, as indicated in section 3.1, some plastics show a pronounced delayed response to deformation, they are said to exhibit a memory. This means that though when the rivet was initially fitted it was a tight fit, a less than tight fit might develop with time following the release of the load on the rivet. Only those plastics which have a good ductility and are not brittle, have high strength and good resistance to creep, are suitable for riveting.

A different version of riveting is known as ultrasonic staking. One of the parts is made with integral rivets, or stakes as they are referred to, projecting from them. These, when mated up with the other part, project through holes in it. Ultrasonics are used to cause the projecting part of the stake to be formed into a mushroom like head and so clamp the two parts together. This type of joining is frequently used when metal parts have to be attached to a plastic, the plastic being made with a stud-like projection and the metal part containing a hole in the relevant position.

5.10   PRESS AND SNAP FITS

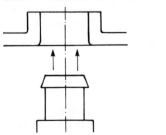

Figure 5.24 A snap-fit

One of the advantages of plastics is that they can be distorted through quite large amounts elastically and still return to their original shape when the load is removed. Press and snap fits rely on this. Such joints may be designed for permanent or recoverable use. Snap fits are stronger and more dependable than press fits, relying on a mechanical interlocking of two components, as well as friction, while press fits rely only on friction.

A common form of snap fit is the hook joint. *Figure 5.24* shows an example of such a snap fit. When the component is pushed into the hole, the end is deformed so that it can slide through the hole until it emerges from the other end. Then it expands and locks the

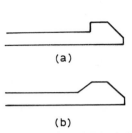

(a)

(b)

Figure 5.25 Hook end type of snap-fit design, (a) for permanent fixing, (b) for recoverable use

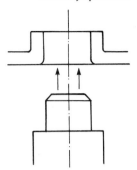

Figure 5.26 A press-fit

component in position. The type of hook end shown in the figure is a permanent type in that it is not possible to disengage it. *Figure 5.25* shows how the hook end varies when it is designed for use as a permanent joint and a recoverable joint. *Figure 5.26* shows a press-fit. The component is a tight fit in the hole.

5.11 THREAD SYSTEMS WITH PLASTICS

Screw threads are one means of joining plastic components, the main problem that can arise is the system coming loose due to the creep of the plastic when under load.

Thread forming screws form the thread by displacement of the plastic when the screw is screwed into a simple hole in the plastic. Self-tapping screws in which the screw cuts its own thread when screwed into the plastic can be used with a greater range of plastics.

5.12 ASSEMBLY

Consider a fairly simple assembly proposition, a bicycle pump. *Figure 5.27* shows the various components that go together to make the pump. The parts are:

(a) A barrel end, made of perhaps p.v.c.;
(b) An insert in the barrel end, made of perhaps brass so that the connector can be screwed into it;
(c) A barrel, made perhaps from a p.v.c. tube;
(d) A handle, made perhaps from polypropylene;
(e) A plunger, made from possibly mild steel;
(f) Two springs, steel;
(g) A screw end cap, made perhaps from polypropylene;
(h) A porté piston, made from polypropylene;
(i) A compression washer, from possibly an artificial rubber.

How should these parts be assembled, in what sequence, so that the entire operation is as quick as possible? You might like to try the exercise yourself with a bicycle pump. One possible assembly sequence is:

(a) Fit insert into barrel end cap.
(b) Fit barrel end cap onto barrel.
(c) Put the barrel with the end cap to one side.
(d) Put the washer on the piston.
(e) Put the porté piston on the piston.

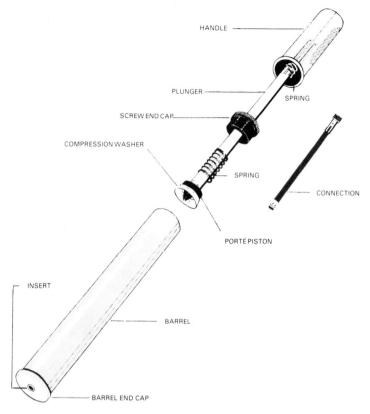

HANDLE

PLUNGER

SPRING

SCREW END CAP

COMPRESSION WASHER

SPRING

CONNECTION

PORTÉ PISTON

INSERT

BARREL

BARREL END CAP

Figure 5.27 The parts of a bicycle pump. (Reproduced by permission of the Engineering Careers Information Service from leaflet *The bicycle pump project.* This is designed to help students explore the materials, processes and operations necessary to make bicycle pump, manufacturing costs, a simple profit and loss account and some development questions)

(f) Put one spring on the piston.
(g) Put the screw end cap on the piston.
(h) Put a spring on the piston.
(i) Put the handle on the piston.
(j) Screw the end cap down onto the barrel.

The final task would probably be to pack the pump, with the connector in a suitable carton.

Some of the operations in the above sequence have to be in that order because it would be very difficult, if not impossible, for that sequence not to occur. Thus, for instance, the sequence with which the items are put on the piston cannot easily be changed if the items are to be in the right places. However it could be feasible to first fit the barrel end cap onto the barrel and then fit the insert into the end cap instead of fitting the insert into the end cap before it is fitted onto the barrel. These different sequences for fitting the insert might however require different fixtures to hold the workpiece during the fitting.

If the assembly is done manually the times taken for each of the operations can be measured and the overall time determined for the entire assembly.

Thus the times might be

(a)	Fit insert into barrel end cap	5 s
(b)	Fit barrel end cap onto barrel	3 s
(c)	Put the barrel with the end cap to one side	1 s
(d)	Put the washer on the piston	2 s
(e)	Put the porté piston on the piston	2 s
(f)	Put one spring on the piston	2 s
(g)	Put the screw end cap on the piston	2 s
(h)	Put a spring on the piston	2 s
(i)	Put the handle on the piston	3 s
(j)	Screw the end cap down onto the barrel	2 s
	Total assembly time	24 s

We can add to this time, perhaps 5 s for picking up the pump and a connector, putting the two together and putting in a carton. This would give a total basic time of 29 s. If we really want to find out how many pumps can be assembled by a worker in a day then we must add to the basic time allowances for relaxation, e.g. the worker perhaps pauses for a few seconds between assembling pumps or needs to blow his or her nose because they have a cold, and contingencies that cannot be easily predetermined, e.g. two springs are tangled together and have to be untangled before they can be fitted. Thus the standard time for the assembly might be 40 s.

By carrying out a prototype assembly it is possible to iron out some of the problems that could occur and perhaps change the sequence of the operations to give a faster assembly, or perhaps the design so that assembly is easier and faster, or perhaps the materials or the production processes used. For instance, it might be better to change the material, and the process, used for the end cap so that there does not have to be separate threaded insert but the piece is made in metal in just one piece. This would then reduce the assembly time; however there might be the point that it would cost more to produce the item this way and so the overall cost of the pump would be higher.

Designing for easier and faster assembly

In any assembly one of the most significant costs is likely to be the cost of the labour involved in assembling the item. The assembly costs are also likely to be a significant factor even when the assembly process is mechanised or automated. Thus designing components so that they can be easily and fastly assembled can have a significant effect on the costs.

With manual assembly, humans are involved rather than machines and humans are flexible enough to deal with irregular situations and make decisions as how to proceed. However, if an assembly operation needs someone to stop, think, make a decision and then adapt to the new situation, there is a time factor involved and hence a cost factor. The more someone needs to be flexible the slower will be the assembly process.

Thus, for instance, in the case of an item requiring electrical wiring, it makes assembly easier if the wires are coloured coded, and perhaps the terminals also colour coded so that a red wire has to be connected to a red terminal. If all the wires, or certainly some of them, were the same colour and there was no help with a

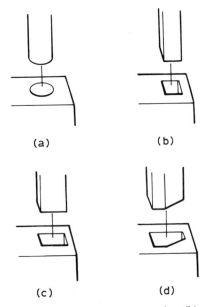

Figure 5.28 (a) Circular cross-section. (b) Square cross-section. (c) Rectangular cross-section. (d) Irregular cross-section

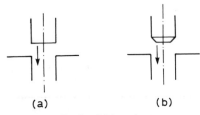

Figure 5.29 Design (b) is easier to assemble than (a)

coding of the terminals then the process would be slower because the person carrying out the assembly would need to think more about which wire was to be connected to which terminal. Colour coding could thus reduce the assembly time, it could also reduce the chance of errors and so the number of products that end up being rejected when inspected.

Another example of how assembly could be made easier and faster is where some component has to be inserted into another in perhaps a particular orientation, marking could again aid. Thus if a tapered tube has to be inserted just one way round into an assembly, marking the end that has to be inserted could reduce the time spent by the person carrying out the assembly in thinking which end is the right one. The marking might be a notch or a groove in this case. Designing the assembly so that either end of the tube could be inserted might however be better.

Figure 5.28 shows a number of situations where one component has to be inserted into another. With the circular cross-section there is complete symmetry and no particular orientation of the component is necessary for it to be inserted into the hole. With the square cross-section there are only a few orientations of the component possible for it to be inserted into the hole. For a rectangular cross-section the number of orientations is even smaller and with the irregular cross-section there is just one orientation. The fewer the ways in which a component can be orientated so that it can be inserted into the hole the longer it will take to carry out the operation. Designing, where possible, so that there are as many orientations as possible for the component gives both easier and faster assembly.

Inserting a circular cross-section rod into a hole may take a significant time in getting the rod just correctly positioned in the right place to slide into the hole. This process can be aided if the edges of the rod, and perhaps the hole, are shaped so that they cause the rod to slide into the right position (*Figure 5.29*).

Jigs and fixtures

A jig is a special device which determines the location dimensions required in some machining or assembly operation. A fixture is a special device that holds the workpiece during machining or assembly. The terms are however not always precisely applied. Jigs and fixtures can make assembly both easier and faster.

Thus, for instance, in an assembly operation where two components have to be welded together, a jig can be used to ensure that the components are correctly located with respect to each other when the weld is made. In the bicycle pump assembly referred to earlier, an insert was put into the barrel end cap. This insert has to be both at the right angle to the surface of the cap and central. This can be ensured by the use of a suitable jig, so designed that the insert can only be put into the cap at the right angle and in the right place.

Some of the basic factors that are considered in the design of jigs and fixtures are:

(a) Location of the workpiece, i.e. ensuring that it is in the right position;
(b) Securing the workpiece while the operations are carried out, i.e. clamping the workpiece;

(c) Location of the tool relative to the workpiece, i.e. ensuring that the operations occur in the right locations;
(d) Support of the workpiece against any forces that are imposed by the process;
(e) Rapid and easy operation.

5.13 MECHANISED ASSEMBLY

The difference between mechanised and automated assembly is that an automated operation is one that not only is mechanised but has the built-in capacity to determine when corrective action is required and then take such action. A mechanised assembly does not have such capacity and ability to take corrective action, it is essentially just using a machine to carry out operations.

The major types of operations that are carried out by machines are workpiece orientation, workpiece transfer and placement, and inspection.

1 Workpiece orientation

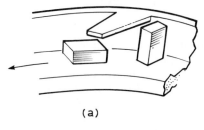

(a)

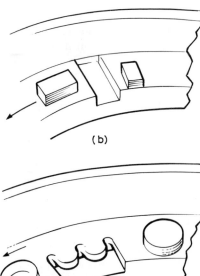

(b)

(c)

A variety of devices are used to ensure the correct orientation of a workpiece for some operations. One widely used method is the vibratory bowl feeder. This is a bowl having an internally inclined track climbing from the base of the bowl to the station at the top of the bowl where the workpiece leaves in the right orientation. The bowl is made to vibrate in a twisting motion. This causes the workpieces to climb the ramp in a series of tiny hops. Along the track, the workpiece encounters devices that will orientate it or reject it back down to the bottom of the bowl because it is in an attitude which does not enable it to be suitably orientated. *Figure 5.30* shows some of these devices.

When the components leave the vibratory bowl feeder they will all be in the same orientation. This orientation can be changed, if required, by changing the angle or the form of the track along which they are fed to the next operation.

Figure 5.30 (a) A wiper, vertical components are deflected off the ramp while horizontal ones are not. (b) A dish-out, components not lying along the track fall out. (c) Components upside down are rejected

Figure 5.31 A feed track with an escapement mechanism

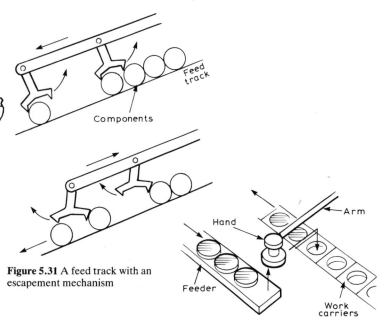

Figure 5.32 A pick-and-place mechanism

2 Workpiece transfer and placement

Means have to be provided for transferring the workpiece from one work station to another and to correctly place the workpiece at each station so that the appropriate operations can be carried out. Feed tracks with perhaps an escapement mechanism might be used (*Figure 5.31*) or pick-and-place mechanisms (*Figure 5.32*). With the feed track and escapement mechanism, the track may be just gravity powered and the escapement a fairly simple device to allow a single component at a time to be released from the track. The rate at which the components are released can, with suitable choice of escapement mechanism, be pre-selected.

The pick-and-place mechanism essentially just involves an arm with a 'hand' for grasping the component. The arm moves the hand out to grasp the component, then pick it up and transfer it to the next work station. A wide variety of mechanisms are possible for workpiece transfer and placement and the above examples are only illustrative of the types of principles involved.

3 Inspection   Inspection can also be mechanised. Thus, for example, containers can be checked to see if they are filled by using, perhaps, a weighing mechanism or a means of determining level of contents within a container. The weighing method may employ a load cell, the level determination might employ a beam of light which becomes blocked if the container is full. In either case the measurement could be used to actuate an accept or reject mechanism.

There may be a considerable number of inspection points in a mechanised assembly process, checking that at each stage the required operation has been carried out properly. Thus if, at one work station, there is a need to spread adhesive on one component face before joining another to it, then an inspection mechanism might be used to check that the adhesive had actually been spread properly before the two components are brought together. Another inspection mechanism might then be used to check that the two components were actually brought together and bonded.

5.14   AUTOMATED ASSEMBLY   A completely automated system would mean that the raw materials were the input to the system and the output was the finished products. While many automated systems have been developed, they usefully operate on only part of the production cycle. Thus there are single work stations which are automated. With such a station a number of operations may be automatically carried out on the product.

A synchronous system, however, consists of the work being moved, perhaps on a rail or an overhead chain conveyor, from one work station to another. At each work station an operation or a number of operations may be carried out. All the workpieces are moved between stations at the same time and over the same distance. The whole line is however controlled by the time required at the slowest operation work station.

A non-synchronous system has the workpiece allowed to spend differing amounts of time at the different work stations, generally by a system which allows the workpiece to be disengaged from the conveyor system at each work station. In order for this system to be effective and keep each work station fully occupied there is a need for buffer stocks to be available.

The continuous system has the workpieces in constant motion and the work stations therefore have to move with the workpiece. This is not always feasible, e.g. with metal removal processes.

The advantages of automated assembly are a reduction in cost per part, increased productivity, more consistent quality, and also the removal of operators from awkward, dirty and perhaps hazardous work areas. However there is generally a high capital cost in setting up an automated system and the more work stations involved the more inefficient the system is likely to be.

Interchangeability

Interchangeability is the appropriate term to describe the assembly process where any one of a batch of components can be used with any one of the mating components. Thus if a shaft is required to fit in a hole in a component, it would not matter which shaft from a batch was chosen nor which component was chosen for it to be fitted in. This is because all the components in a particular batch are interchangeable. In order to achieve this, the tolerances of the components must be specified to the standard required to suit the type of fit required.

An alternative to this is to use selective assembly. This involves the components in any batch being graded for size. Mating components can then be chosen from those size groups that will provide the type of fit required. This type of assembly is particularly feasible where mechanised or automated assembly and inspection is involved.

5.15 LIMITS AND FITS

There are a number of terms associated with the specification of components that are to fit together.

1 Basic size The basic size is the nominal size specified by the designer. This cannot however be produced exactly because of the inherent variations within the production process. It is the size by reference to which the limits of the size are specified, the same basic size being specified for both members of the fit.

2 Limits The limits of the size are the maximum and minimum sizes permitted for the dimension concerned, the maximum limit of size being the greater of the two limits and the minimum limit the smaller of the two (*Figure 5.33*).

3 Tolerance The tolerance is the difference between the maximum and minimum limits of size.

4 Fit Fit is the term used to describe the relationship resulting from the difference, before assembly, between the sizes of the two parts which are to be assembled. A clearance fit is one which always provides a clearance, i.e. the tolerance zone of the hole is entirely above that of the shaft (*Figure 5.34a*). An interference fit is one that always provides an interference, i.e. the difference between the sizes of the hole and the shaft before assembly is negative. This means that the tolerance zone of the hole is entirely below that of the shaft (*Figure 5.34b*). A transition fit is one which may provide either a clearance or an interference, the tolerance zones of the hole and the shaft overlap (*Figure 5.34c*).

5 The hole basis of fits The hole basis of fits is the system of fits in which the different clearances and interferences are all obtained

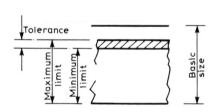

Figure 5.33 Limits for a shaft

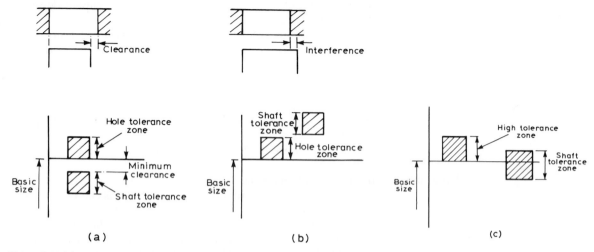

Figure 5.34 (a) A clearance fit, (b) an interference fit, (c) a transition fit

by associating different shafts with a single hole. *Figure 5.34* uses the principle in that all the shaft fits are considered in relationship to a constant, single hole. This system is the one most commonly used, an alternative being to associate different holes with a single shaft.

6 Deviations The deviation is the algebraic difference between a size and the corresponding basic size. The term upper deviation is used for the algebraic difference between the maximum limit of size and the corresponding basic size. The lower deviation is the algebraic difference between the minimum limit of the size and the corresponding basic size (*Figure 5.35*).

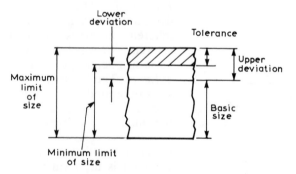

Figure 5.35 Deviations

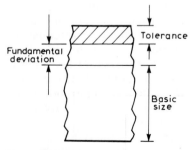

Figure 5.36 Fundamental deviation

7 Fundamental deviation The fundamental deviation is that one of the upper or lower deviation, being the one nearest to the basic size, which can define the position of the tolerance zone. It is thus the deviation of the tolerance band away from the basic size (*Figure 5.36*). The fundamental deviation is positive when the deviation is added onto the basic size to give the position of the tolerance band. Thus the shaft in *Figure 5.36* has a positive fundamental deviation. A negative fundamental deviation means that the deviation has to be subtracted from the basic size to give the tolerance band. Thus an interference fit will have a positive fundamental deviation, a clearance fit will have a negative fundamental deviation. A transitional fit can have either a positive or a negative fundamental deviation.

The ISO system

Tolerance is a measure of the quality of the fit, the smaller the tolerance the higher the quality. However to maintain a constant quality over a range of basic sizes the tolerances need to be varied, a constant tolerance whatever the basic size would not give the same quality. For example, while a tolerance of 0.120 mm on a 50 mm diameter shaft would give a certain quality, the same quality on a 200 mm diameter shaft would require 0.160 mm tolerance. The larger the basic size the larger the tolerance for the same quality.

Figure 5.37 shows the type of relationship that exists between tolerance and size for a particular quality. Over the diameter range 30–50 mm a tolerance of 0.100 mm, the range 50–80 mm a tolerance of 0.120 mm, over the range 80–120 mm a tolerance of 0.140 mm—all these will give approximately the same quality. A range of these graphs can be drawn for different qualities. The ISO system provides a series of tolerance grades, each grade corresponding to a particular quality. The grade corresponding to the values given in *Figure 5.37* is designated grade IT 10. By just specifying this tolerance grade, the tolerances for any diameter shaft can be found using tables, derived from the equation for the graph, and all will give the same quality. Tolerance grades are always prefixed by the letter IT and range from IT 01, IT 0, IT 1, IT 2, IT 3 to IT 16, a total of 18 grades, the earlier in this grade sequence the finer the quality.

When selecting a fit to be used for a given application it is necessary to choose an appropriate fundamental deviation and the appropriate tolerances for the mating parts. These choices will then determine the type of fit, i.e. the amount of clearance or interference. As with tolerances, fundamental deviations are a function of basic size. The ISO system provides 41 different fundamental deviation grades, within each grade the fundamental deviation varying with size to give the same fit characteristic.

The fundamental deviation grades are represented by a single or pair of letters, with capital letters being used for holes and lower case letters for shafts. Thus for holes we have grades, A,B,C,CD,D,E,EF,F,FG,G, etc, while for shafts the grades are a,b,c,cd,d,e,ef,f,fg,g, etc. Letter grades below h or H represent negative deviations while the letters above h or H represent positive deviations. The letter a represents a large negative deviation while the letter z a large positive deviation. The letter h, or H, is zero fundamental deviation.

For each fundamental deviation grade, tables are available to give the deviations within each grade for different basic size ranges. Thus, for instance, the tables give for a shaft in the size range over 30 mm to 40 mm with grade c, an upper deviation of −0.120 mm. For negative deviations the upper deviation is the fundamental deviation. For a shaft in the size range over 30 mm to 40 mm with grade y, the tables give a lower deviation of +0.094 mm. For positive deviations the lower deviation is the fundamental deviation.

In order to specify the fit it is necessary to quote both the

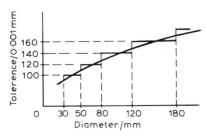

Figure 5.37 Tolerance values for the same quality

tolerance grade and the fundamental deviation grade. The fit is thus specified by combining both the grade designations in the form H7 or e9, the letter indicating the fundamental deviation grade and the number the tolerance grade. For a shaft e9, the tables give for a shaft in the size range 30 mm to 50 mm:

Upper deviation   −0.050 mm
Tolerance   0.062 mm

Thus for a shaft of basic diameter 35 mm the upper limit is −0.050 mm and the lower limit is −(0.050 + 0.062) = −0.102 mm.

Working to the hole basis of fits means that the shafts are all considered in relation to a basic hole size. Because of this the hole basis means that the holes are all designated in terms of the H grade as this is the grade with zero fundamental deviation. Thus the hole for which the e9 shaft might be used with could be, say, H7. The tables give for a hole in the size range 30 to 50 mm:

Lower deviation   0
Tolerance   0.025 mm

Thus for a hole of basic diameter 35 mm the lower limit is 0 and the upper limit ×0.025 mm.

Figure 5.38 shows the data for H7 hole with the e9 shaft. The minimum clearance is 0.127 mm. The fit is a clearance fit.

A very wide range of tolerances and fundamental differences can be selected within the ISO system to give many different fit conditions. However the majority of fit conditions required for normal engineering can be provided by a small selection of grades. The following are the selection:

Holes   H7,H8,H9,H11
Shafts   c11,d10,e9,f7,g6,h6,k6,n6,p6,s6

Clearance fits are given by combining any of the above holes with shafts c11,d10,e9,f7,g6,h6. Transition fits are given by combining H7 with k6 or n6 and interference fits by combining H7 with p6 or s6.

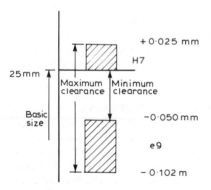

Figure 5.38 H7 hole with e9 shaft

QUESTIONS

(1) What advantages can the use of adhesives have over other methods of joining metals?
(2) What factors can determine the time taken to make an adhesive bonded joint and hence the rate of production?
(3) How does soldering differ from brazing?
(4) How should the design of a brazed joint differ from that used for welding?
(5) State two of the problems that may occur when welding is used to make a joint.
(6) State four factors that should be taken into account in the choice of a welding process.
(7) What factors determine the optimum fastening system to use?
(8) Under what circumstances might a tubular rivet be used in preference to a solid rivet?

(9) For what purposes might eyelets be used?

(10) Suggest joining methods that might be used to (a) join two sheets of metal face-to-face together, (b) attach a metal clip to a flat metal surface, (c) join two thick steel bars, (d) join two steel sheets edge-to-edge or with a slight overlap, (e) attach leather to a metal frame.

(11) Can (a) thermoplastics, (b) thermosets, be welded?

(12) Explain how hot-plate welding is used to join two plastic components.

(13) What characteristics does a plastic to have if it is to be successfully joined using metal rivets?

(14) Explain the process of ultrasonic staking.

(15) How do snap fits differ from press fits?

(16) Suggest joining methods that might be used to (a) fix a metal clip on the face of a sheet of plastic, (b) join two thermoplastic pipes, (c) bond two sheets of thermoset materials together, face-to-face, (d) join two sheets of thermoplastic materials along a line.

(17) A small toy truck consists of the following parts: a wooden body, two metal axle rods to pass through holes in the body, four wheels with central holes to slide over axle, four caps to fit on the ends of the axle and prevent the wheels falling off, four washers to go on the axles between the wheels and the body and prevent the wheels binding against the body, two metal discs to be stuck on the front of the car as headlights, two pieces of red plastic to stick on the rear as tail lights, two strips of metal foil to be stuck on as bumpers, a strip of plastic to be stuck on as a windscreen. Suggest a possible sequence for assembling the toy truck.

(18) List all the parts that constitute a bicycle and propose an assembly sequence. Assume that the wheel assemblies have been pre-assembled.

(19) Select a product and plan the assembly of it from its constituent parts. Possible products could be a table lamp, a 13 A plug, a telephone handpiece, etc.

(20) The bicycle pump shown in *Figure 5.27* includes a barrel end made of p.v.c. and an insert into that end, made of brass, so that the connector can be screwed into it. Suggest another possible way that end piece could be manufactured. How would someone go about comparing the costs of the two methods, what factors would they have to consider?

(21) Give two examples of design changes that could make assembly easier and faster.

(22) The three basic elements of mechanised assembly can be considered to be workpiece orientation, workpiece transfer and placement, and inspection. Explain briefly the type of operations involved in each element.

(23) State three advantages of automated assembly over manual assembly.

(24) What are the basic characteristics of the automated systems termed (a) single work station, (b) synchronous system, (c) non-synchronous system, (d) continuous system.

(25) An assembly process might be termed a selective assembly or an interchangeability system. Explain the difference.

(26) Explain the following terms as used in limits and fits, (a)

basic size, (b) limit, (c) tolerance, (d) fit, (e) fundamental deviation.

(27) Distinguish between a clearance fit, an interference fit and a transitional fit.

(28) Tolerance/0.001 mm

Basic size		IT 8	IT 9	IT 10
Over	*To*			
mm	mm			
10	18	33	52	70
18	30	39	62	84
30	50	46	74	100

Fundamental deviations for shafts/0.001 mm

Basic size		*Upper deviation*	
Over	*To*	d	e
mm	mm		
10	18	−50	−32
18	30	−65	−40
30	50	−80	−50

For the following shaft-hole combinations determine the tolerance, the lower and upper limits, the minimum and maximum clearances: (a) e9 with H8, basic size 15 mm, (b) d10 with H9, basic size 30 mm, (c) e9 with H9, basic size 35 mm.

6 Assignments

The aims of this chapter are to integrate the topic as a whole by asking you to analyse component designs and recommend an appropriate method of manufacture, taking account of cost and quality.

6.1 RESTRICTIONS IMPOSED BY DESIGN

There are a number of vital questions which need to be posed before a decision is made as regards to the manufacturing process to be used for a produt.

1 What is the material?

The type of material to be used affects the choice of processing method. Thus, for example, if casting is to be used and the material has a high melting point then the process must be either sand casting or investment casting.

2 What is the shape?

The shape of the product is generally a vital factor in determining which type of process can be used. Thus, for example, a product in the form of a tube could be produced by centrifugal casting, drawing or extrusion but not generally by other methods.

3 What type of detail is involved?

Has the product to have holes, threads, inserts, hollow sections, fine detail etc? Thus, for example, forging could not be used if there was a requirement for hollow sections.

4 What dimensional accuracy and tolerances are required?

High accuracy would rule out sand casting, though investment casting might well be suitable.

5 Are any finishing processes to be used?

Has the process to be used to give the product in its final finished state or will there have to be an extra finishing process. Thus, for example, planing will not produce as smooth a surface as grinding.

6 What quantities are involved?

Is the product a one-off, a small batch, a large batch, continuous production? While some processes are economic for small quantities, others do not become economic until large quantities are involved. Thus open die forging could be economic for small numbers but closed die forging would not be economic unless large numbers were produced.

6.2 THE COST ASPECTS OF PROCESS SELECTION

With sand casting a new mould has to be made for each product manufactured. With die casting the same mould can be used for a large number of components but the initial die cost is high. Which process would be the cheapest if say 10 products were required, or perhaps 1000 products?

The manufacturing cost, for any process, can be considered to be made up of two elements—fixed costs and variable costs. The fixed cost might, for instance, include the cost of making the die.

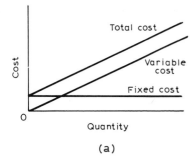

(a)

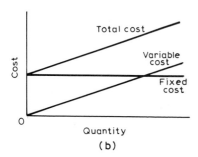

(b)

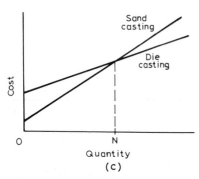

(c)

Figure 6.1 (a) Sand casting costs. (b) Die casting costs. (c) Total costs compared

The fixed cost is the cost which is incurred regardless of the quantity of products that are manufactured. The variable cost will include the cost of the material used in a particular product. In the case of the sand casting it includes the non-reusable parts of the mould. The variable costs are thus the costs associated with each product and depend on the quantity of product produced. To illustrate this, consider the way in which the fixed and the variable costs might appear for the two processes, sand casting and die casting. *Figure 6.1* shows the graphs of costs against quantity for the two processes and how their total costs compare.

For the die casting there is a higher fixed cost than for the sand casting, due to the cost of the die. The sand casting has however a greater cost per item produced. The comparison graph shows that up to a quantity N sand casting is the cheaper but that for quantities greater than N die casting is the cheaper process.

Capital costs for installations, e.g. the cost of a machine or even a foundry, are usually defrayed over an expected life time of the installation. However in any one year there will be depreciation of the asset and this is the capital cost that is defrayed against the output of the product in that year. Thus if the capital expenditure needed to purchase a machine and instal it was, say, £50 000, then in one year a depreciation of 10% might be used and thus £5000 defrayed as capital cost against the quantity of product produced in that year.

Consider, as an example, a product to be made from a thermoplastic. It is to be hollow and of fairly simple form. It can be made by injection moulding or rotational moulding (other methods are also possible but for the purpose of this example only these two alternatives are considered). The cost of the installation for injection moulding is £90 000, the cost for the rotational moulding, using a fairly simple form of the equipment, is £10 000. Thus if these installations depreciate at 10% per year then the costs per year are—injection moulding £9000 and rotational moulding £1000. If these installations are to be used in the year to only make the product we are concerned with, then these charges in their entirety constitute an element of the fixed costs.

Another element of the fixed costs is the cost of the dies or tools needed specifically for the product concerned. In the case of the injection moulding the cost is £2000 and for the rotational moulding £500.

Other factors we could include in the fixed costs are plant maintenance and tool or die overhaul. However, considering just the above two charges, for the installation when we assume that it only produces the above product per year and for the specific tooling if only used for the one production run, we have:

	Injection moulding	*Rotational moulding*
Installation cost	£9000	£1000
Die costs	£2000	£500
Total fixed cost	£11000	£1500

The variable cost are the material costs, the labour costs, the power costs, and any finishing costs required. These might appear, per unit produced, as follows:

	Injection moulding	*Rotational moulding*
Direct labour cost	£0.30	£1.40
Other labour costs; e.g. supervision	£0.15	£0.30
Power costs	£0.06	£0.15
Finishing costs	£1.00	zero
Materials costs	£0.40	£0.40
Total variable cost	£1.91	£2.25

If 1000 units are required then the costs will be:

	Injection moulding	*Rotational moulding*
Fixed costs	£11000	£1500
Variable costs	£1910	£2250
Total cost	£12910	£3750

On the basis of the above costings the rotational moulding is considerably cheaper than the injection moulding. The injection moulding installation can however produce 50 items per hour and the use in one year of this to just produce 1000 items is a considerable underuse of the asset. The rotational moulding installation can however only produce 2 items per hour.

Thus if the rotational moulding installation was perhaps only used for this product but the injection moulding installation was used for a number of products, then the injection moulding installation cost would be defrayed over a greater number of products and thus that element of the fixed cost defrayed against the product would be less.

The questions to be asked when costing a product are:
1 Is the installation to be solely used for the product concerned?
The purpose of this question is to determine whether the entire capital cost has to be written off against the product or whether it can be spread over a number of products.
2 Is the tooling to be used solely for the product concerned?
If specific tooling has to be developed then the entire cost will have to be put against the product.
3 What are the direct labour costs per item?
4 What are the other labour costs involved?
In this category consider supervision costs, inspection costs, labouring costs, setting costs, etc.
5 What is the power cost?
6 Are there any finishing processes required—if so, what are their costs?
7 What are the materials costs?
8 Are there any overhead costs to be included?

6.3 MAKE OR BUY DECISIONS

In considering the production needed for a product, a decision that may be needed is whether components should be made within the company or bought in from outside suppliers. It may be that these suppliers will have to specially make the components to the specified design or it may be that the components are standard and can be purchased from stock. The deciding factor as to which is the right alternative is likely to be the cost. If the component can be

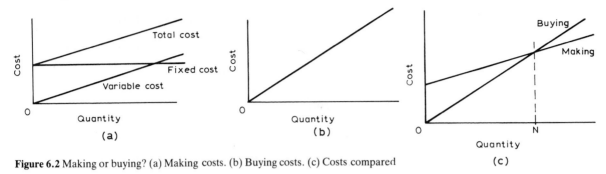

Figure 6.2 Making or buying? (a) Making costs. (b) Buying costs. (c) Costs compared

bought cheaper than it can be made then it is likely that it will be bought rather than made.

Figure 6.2 illustrates on a cost-quantity graph the effects on cost of making or buying in a particular example. The cost of making involves a high fixed cost (for the plant required) and a variable cost for each item produced. Buying, if a standard item, involves no fixed cost but only a variable cost. This variable cost per item is greater than the variable cost per item if the component was made in company. At a particular quantity N the costs for making and buying are the same, below that point the buying cost is less than the making cost, above that point the making cost is less than the buying cost. The vital questions to be posed are:

1 Is it cheaper to make or buy the component for the quantity required?
2 If it is cheaper to buy, are there any other reasons why you should not buy?

6.4 QUALITY   In general, the higher the quality the more it costs. With any particular process there is a technological limit to the accuracy that can be achieved and the nearer that process is used to that limit the more it will cost. A different process might be more cost effective at such accuracies because it is not near its technological limit. With any process there will invariably be a variation in the quality of the output, some processes tending to have a greater variability than others. Thus the requirement for a high quality might only be met by having a large number of rejects, as not reaching the required quality. This will have cost implications.

Quality control also costs money. A high quality requirement is likely to mean a high level of inspection, to ensure that the quality is maintained. The obvious questions that have to be posed of any product design are:

1 Is the specified quality really necessary?
2 Do all aspects of the design have to be to the specified quality, e.g. accurate independent locations of three holes may not be necessary but just accuracy in the relationship of the hole positions between themselves?

6.5 ASSIGNMENTS   (1) A 13 A plug
(a) Dismantle a 13 A plug and list all the component parts and the types of materials that have been used for them;
(b) For each component, give reasons for the material used and the shape of the component;

(c) For each component state the possible manufacturing methods;

(d) Compare the merits of the manufacturing methods bearing in mind that the plugs are to be produced in very large quantities;

(e) Propose an assembly sequence for the plug.

(2) A gearwheel

The Open University Technology, second level course on Engineering Materials, T252, Unit 2, considers the production processes feasible for a small gearwheel in a food mixer, considering the following alternatives:

(a) Pressure die casting using zinc;

(b) Sintering using iron;

(c) Injection moulding using nylon;

(d) Extrusion using aluminium (and then slicing);

(e) Gravity die casting using aluminium;

(f) Machining using mild steel.

A large quantity has to be produced and the cost must be as low as is consistent with a reliable, trouble-free, gearwheel in service. The cheapest process they found was pressure die casting using zinc, however the manufacturer uses sintering with iron, the second cheapest process.

Explain the restrictions imposed by the gearwheel design upon the manufacturing methods. Explain the restrictions imposed on the material used by the service requirements. Compare the alternatives listed above. Why do you think the manufacturer chose sintering using iron?

(3) A container for liquids

Figure 6.3 shows the basic design form for a container for concentrated still drinks. It is required in very large quantities, the proposed material being high density polyethylene. Blow moulding and rotational moulding have been proposed.

(a) Compare the two proposed processes. In view of the large numbers required, which of them would be likely to be the most economic?

(b) What restrictions are imposed on the design by these processes?

(4) A push cap

Figure 6.4 shows a simple cap designed to lock onto the end of small shafts, the barb being to prevent the cap coming off. The cap is to be made from metal?

(a) What processes can be used to manufacture the push cap?

(b) If the cap is wanted in large quantities, which would be the most economic method?

(c) Would your answer to (b) be changed if only small quantities had been required?

(5) An electrical screwdriver

A proposed design involves a steel blade mounted in a plastic

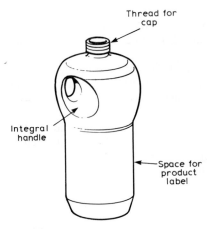

Thread for cap

Integral handle

Space for product label

Figure 6.3 Container for liquids

Barb

Figure 6.4 Push cap

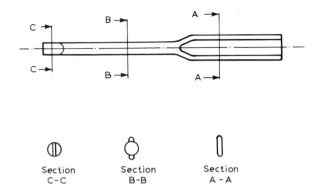

Figure 6.5 Screwdriver blade

handle, cellulose acetate—a transparent thermoplastic being proposed for the handle. An important consideration is that when the handle of the screwdriver is rotated that the blade rotates with the handle and not within the handle. For this reason the blade has a flattened cross-section for that part within the handle (*Figure 6.5*). The screwdrivers are to be produced in very large quantities and must be at a low cost in order to compete in the market place with other manufacturer's screwdrivers.

(a) What are the restrictions imposed on the manufacturing processes for the blade and the handle by the design?

(b) Suggest possible processes for manufacturing the blade and the handle.

(c) Which of the processes would you consider on cost and quality considerations to be the optimum ones?

(d) How will the blade be fixed in the handle?

(6) A bicycle frame

The frame of a bicycle could be made of tubular mild steel welded together or produced in one piece, perhaps by casting.

(a) Compare these two methods of producing bicycle frames. Consider all the processes that would be involved in going from raw material to finished goods.

(b) Which method is likely to be most economic?

(c) If you were a manufacturer of bicycle frames and opted for the welding together of tubular mild steel, what factors would you need to take into account in deciding whether to make your own tube or buy in the tube?

(7) A reinforcement plate

Figure 6.6 shows a simple reinforcement plate made out of sheet mild steel. Shearing or machining are two possible methods of producing the item from sheet metal.

(a) Compare these methods, bearing in mind the cost factor, if large quantities are to be produced.

(b) In the case of shearing, how can the amount of scrap be minimized?

(c) If a few non-standard versions of the plate were required, which method would be the most economic?

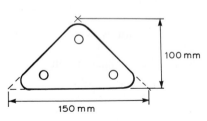

Figure 6.6 Reinforcement plate

(8) A spanner
Forging, casting or machining from the solid have been proposed as methods that could be used to produce spanners.
(a) With forging, what would be the optimum method if the spanners were required in large quantities?
(b) With casting, what would be the optimum method if the spanners were required in large quantities?
(c) Compare forging, casting and machining for the production of spanners where they are required in large quantities. Which method would be likely to give the cheapest product?
(d) Which of the processes would lead to the most scrap?

(9) Machining or powder techniques?
Your company makes a large number of items by machining, some of them being relatively simple jobs and some complex, involving compound curves and intricate surface features. A proposal has been made that powder techniques should be

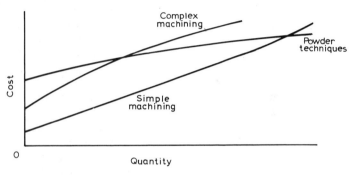

Figure 6.7 Costs of machining and powder techniques

used for much of the work that is currently machined. It has been suggested that the relationship between cost and quantity of any product manufactured is, for the various processes, of the form shown in *Figure 6.7*.
(a) Present arguments justifying, or rejecting, the graphs shown in *Figure 6.7*.
(b) What limitations on the designs possible are posed by the use of powder techniques?

(10) A retainer ring
Figure 6.8 shows the proposed design for a retaining clip, of hardened and tempered carbon steel. The surfaces must be smooth with no sharp corners on the inner circumferential edges.
(a) What processes could be used to manufacture the item?
(b) What would be the most economic method if 4000 items were required?

Figure 6.8 A retainer ring. Only the nominal dimensions, to give an order of size, have been given

(11) A car dashboard
A car dashboard has to be formed to a variety of contours, have holes for instruments, various control knobs and generally a glove compartment. Both metal and plastic have been used.

(a) What processes are possible for the forming of the dashboard? State for each process whether the dashboard can be made in one piece, in one operation.

(b) Discuss the economics of the various processes.

(c) For some of the components that are attached to a dashboard, what fixing methods can be used?

(12) A machine tool base

A base for a special machine tool has to be made, only one having to be produced. Two proposals have been made, one to make a gray iron casting and the other to make it of steel and weld together the various parts after machining. The casting will be twice the weight of the fabricated one.

(a) Compare the two methods proposed for the base.

(b) For the casting, the cost of making a sand pattern is £400, the labour costs, with overheads, for the making of the casting is £840, and the materials cost £250. For the fabricated base, the cost of the machining, including overheads, is £300, the cost of the welding, including overheads, is £500 with an extra £50 being required for the cost of the electrode material consumed during the welding, and the cost of the material is £120. Which method is the most economical?

(c) Before the base can be made, it is realised there could be a market for a small number of these bases. Plot graphs showing how the cost varies with quantity and comment on the significance of the graphs in the determination of the optimum manufacturing method.

(13) Rubber washers

Rubber washers are moulded in the thousands. However this process leaves a flash which has to be subsequently removed. In *Engineering*, June 1983 issue, it is reported that Syke Instrumentation with British Aerospace had adapted a robot to carry out the loading of a machine for the flash removal operation.

(a) What moulding process is likely to be used?

(b) What alternatives to moulding are there?

(c) What process is likely to be used for the removal of the flash?

(d) Before the robot can be used to transfer a washer to the flash removal machine, a feeding hopper has to be used to ensure that only one washer at a time is presented to the robot. Outline a possible form for this hopper.

(e) Outline the full automated sequence of operations, from moulding to the final washer production.

(14) A window frame

It is proposed to make long lengths of a suitable section which can then be cut up into appropriate lengths and joined to make metal window frames. The proposal is to use steel.

(a) What processes could be used to produce such a section?

(b) What processes could be used to join the sections at the corners to form the window frames? Would you envisage that special corner pieces would be needed, if so—how will they be made?

(c) Compare the processes you suggest in (a) and (b) for quality, fixed and variable costs, and facilities required.

(15) A can
Cans are used for both soft and alcoholic drinks, the cans being made of aluminium.
(a) The cans could be produced in one piece, with the sole exception of the lid, and having no seam. What processes could be used for this?
(b) An alternative is to fabricate the can, with the walls and the base being separate and the can having a joining seam for the walls. What processes could be used for this?
(c) Compare and contrast the two manufacturing methods described by (a) and (b). Consider which one is likely to be the most economic.
(d) How could the lid be attached?
(e) The lid is to have a pull ring for producing an opening in the lid. How could this be produced?

Appendix: Safety

The *Health and Safety at Work Act, 1974* consists of three parts. The first part contains the Health and Safety at Work provisions. This part has 54 sections, each subdivided into numbered sub-sections and paragraphs. The following are some of the sections relevant to safe working practice.

Section 2 states that it is the duty of every employer to ensure, as far as is reasonably practical, the health, safety and welfare at work of all their employees. This includes, for example:
(a) the provision and maintenance of plant and systems of work that are safe and without risk to health;
(b) arrangements for ensuring safety and absence of risks to health in connection with the use, handling, storage, and transport of articles and substances;
(c) the maintenance of any place of work under the employer's control in a condition that is safe and without risks to health, and the provision and maintenance of safe access and egress from it;
(d) the provision and maintenance of a working environment for their employees that is safe, without risks to health, and adequate as regards facilities and arrangements for their welfare at work.

Section 3 places a general duty on employers to ensure that their activities do not endanger persons not in their employment.

Section 4 places a general duty on persons in relation to those who are not their employees, to ensure that plant made available to them is safe and without risk to health.

Section 6 places duties on anyone who designs, manufactures, imports, supplies or instals an article or substance for use at work, to ensure that it is safe and without risk to health.

Section 7 places duties on employees to take reasonable care to ensure that they do not endanger themselves, or anyone else, who may be affected by their work activities.

Section 8 places a duty on all persons not to misuse anything provided in the interests of health and safety purposes under a statutory agreement.

The *Factories Act, 1961* requires all dangerous parts of machinery to be securely fenced. In addition there are specific regulations for different types of machinery, all concerned with ensuring the safety of employees in the use of machinery.

Specific requirements for mechanical power presses are contained in the *Power Presses Regulations, 1965 and 1972*. They apply to a press or press brake which is power driven and includes a flywheel and a clutch mechanism, they do not however apply to hydraulic or pneumatic presses, guillotines, combination punching and shearing machines, upsetting machines, and other similar machines. These other machines are covered by the Factories Act but not the specific Power Press Regulations. The following are some of the more important aspects of the regulations.

(a) Only persons who have attained the age of 18 and are appointed by the company by means of an entry in or a certificate attached to a special register may carry out the setting, resetting, adjustment or trying out of tools, the installation or adjustment of any safety device and the day-to-day inspection and testing of safety devices. The person who is to perform these duties must receive practical training on power press mechanisms, safety devices, accident causation and prevention, the work and duties of the tool setter and tool design. The entry in the register must state the presses or types of press for which the person has been appointed and the operations for which the appointment has been made.

(b) Each press must be distinctly marked so that it can be identified in the register, similarly all guards for tools should be marked. Every press tool must have the maximum flywheel speed and the direction of rotation of the flywheel conspicuously marked on the press.

(c) The Press Regulations also require a thorough examination of all newly installed power presses and newly installed guards or safety devices, a thorough examination of presses using other than fixed guards every 6 months, a thorough examination every 12 months of presses having only fixed guards, inspection of safety devices every time tools and/or guards are set, reset or adjusted, and inspection of safety devices within 4 hours of the start of each working shift. These examinations must be carried out by a competent person, this usually meaning an appropriately qualified engineer, surveyor of an insurance company or a company specialising in such work.

(d) Guards must be secure, preventing all contact by the machine operator with dangerous parts of that machine. They must be kept in position while the dangerous parts are in motion and should not be capable of being removed or adjusted without the use of tools, so making it more difficult for an inexperienced person or the operator to remove or adjust them.

Special requirements of machines using abrasive wheels are set out in the *Abrasive Wheels Regulations, 1970 and 1974*. The following are some of the more important aspects of those regulations.

(a) The precautions that must be taken when examining, storing, handling, selecting, mounting, truing and dressing wheels are specified, also the training of persons to mount wheels, guards and work-rests.

(b) Every abrasive wheel with a diameter more than 55 mm must be marked with the maximum permissible speed in revolutions per minute and the working speed of every grinding machine specified in a notice clearly visible and attached to the machine.

(c) Guards must be provided and kept in position, unless exceptionally the nature of the work precludes their use.

The *Horizontal Milling Machine Regulations, 1928*, set out the specific requirements of the milling process. In any milling set up there must be effective guarding of the cutter, this means completely enclosing the cutter while the machine is in use. It is important to have the cutter stationary when the workpiece is being inserted, adjusted or removed, when swarf is being removed, during cleaning and when the cutting oil or coolant supply pipe is being adjusted or cleaned.

The *Protection of Eyes Regulation, 1974*, states that employers must provide eye protection for every employee who works in any of the specified processes, e.g. grinding, and that a person provided with eye protectors or a shield must make full and proper use of it.

Further reading

1 Publications of the Engineering Industry Training Board (54 Clarendon Road, Watford WD1 1LB)
The following, among their very long list of useful publications, are specially relevant:
EITB Engineering Technicians Guide: Costing TG25
EITB Training Element, Introduction to the Power Press EA9
EITB Training Element, A guide to the statutory power press Regulations 1965 and 1972, EG9
EITB Training Element, Accidents—their causes and prevention in the press shop, EG11
EITB Training Element, Safe Milling Practice, EG52
EITB Training Element, Mounting of Abrasive Wheels, EG66

2 *Engineering Design Guides*, published for the Design Council, the British Standards Institution and the Council of Engineering Institutions by Oxford University Press. The following of their guides are particularly relevant:
01 Introduction to fastening systems
02 Adhesive bonding
03 Miscellaneous fasteners
06 Welding Processes
10 Brazing
11 Metal forming I: forging and related processes
12 Metal forming II: pressing and related processes
17 The engineering properties of plastics
24 Plastics mouldings

3 Manual of British Standards in *Engineering Drawing and Design*, British Standards Institution in association with Hutchinson (1984)

4 The Open University.
Technology, a second level course, Engineering Materials: an introduction—Unit 2 Putting materials to work (T252).
Technology, a third level course, Materials processing; Unit 10 Casting processes; Unit 11 Polymer processing; Unit 12 Working solids; Unit 13 Joining and shaping; Unit 15 Finishing processes.